Power Maths

Year 1 Practice Book A

What do you look like?
Draw a picture of you.

This book belongs to _____ .

My class is _____ .

Contents

We will practise different ways to solve problems!

Now let's practise!

How to use this book

Let's see how this Practice Book works!

Use the Textbook first to learn how to solve this type of problem.

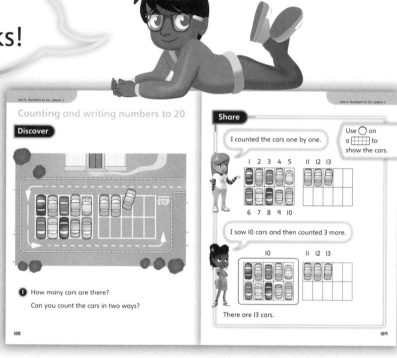

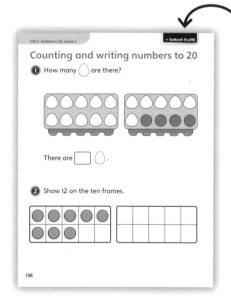

This shows you which Textbook page to use.

Have a go at questions by yourself using this Practice Book. Use what you have learned.

Challenge questions make you think hard!

Questions with this light bulb make you think differently.

Reflect

Each lesson ends with a Reflect question so you can show how much you have learned.

Show what you have done in My Power Points at the back of this book.

Reflect

Think about what you have learned today.

- Today I have learned _____
- _____
- _____
- _____

My journal

At the end of a unit your teacher will ask you to fill in My Journal.

This will help you show how much you can do now that you have finished the unit.

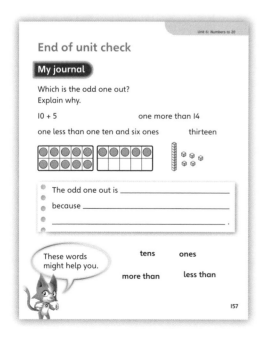

Unit 6: Numbers to 20

End of unit check

My journal

Which is the odd one out? Explain why.

10 + 5	one more than 14
one less than one ten and six ones	thirteen

- The odd one out is _____
- because _____
- _____.

These words might help you.

tens	ones
more than	less than

157

Unit 6: Numbers to 20

Power check

How do you feel about your work?

Power puzzle

Complete the puzzle so every box has a different number.

| 9 | < | | < | 19 |

↓ One more   ↓ One less

| | < | | < | |

↓ One more   ↓ One less

| | < | | < | |

158

→ Textbook 1A p8

Sorting objects

1 Sort into groups. Circle each group.

a)

c)

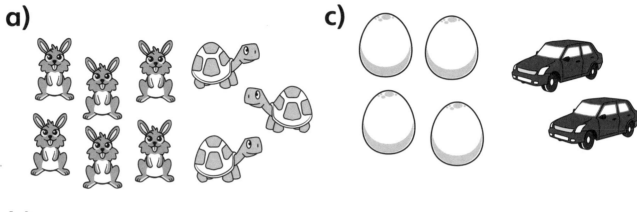

b)

2 Sort into groups. Circle each group.

a)

b)

3 Sort into groups.

a)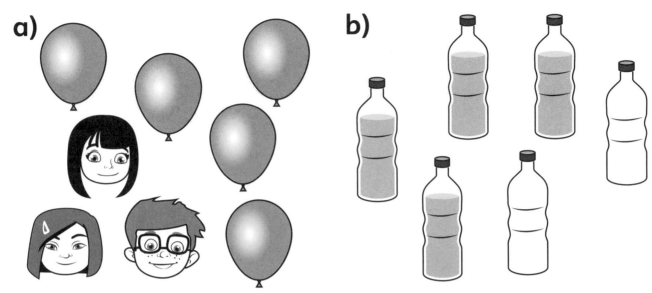

b)

4 Which one doesn't belong?

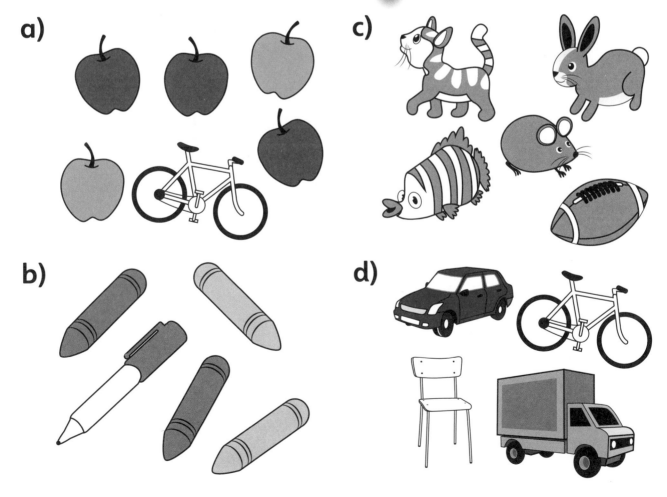

a)

b)

c)

d)

5 Sort the objects. Tell a partner how you sorted them.

Can you find another way?

Reflect

Look around your classroom. What objects can you see?
Can you sort some of the objects into groups?
Draw the groups.

Counting objects to 10

1 Count, then match each picture with its number.

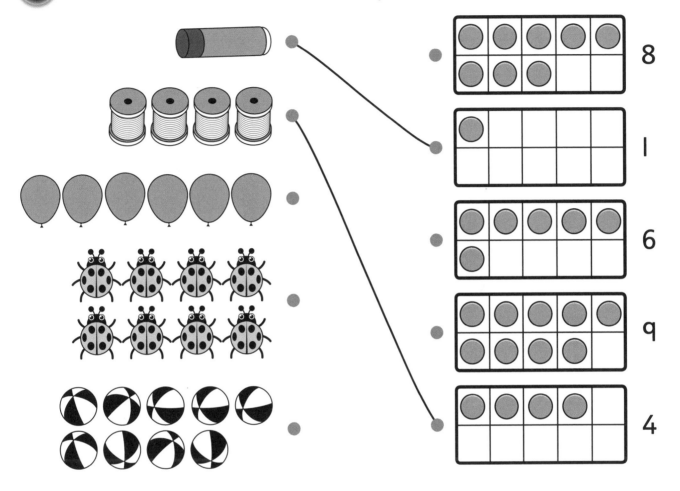

2 Count, then colour counters to match.

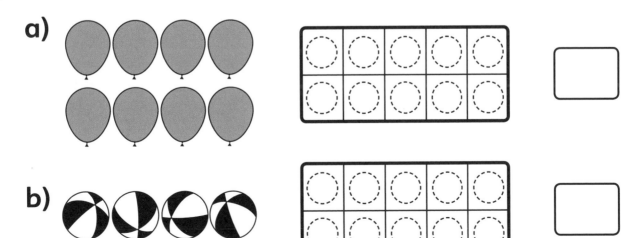

a)

b)

3 **a)** Colour in 7 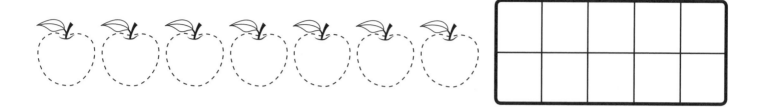.

b) Colour in 5 .

4 How many  are there?

I think there are 3.

Count carefully!

There are ☐ .

5 How many ways can you show me 10?

CHALLENGE

Show a friend. Are there any other ways?

Reflect

Pick a number. How can you show it?

My number is ⬚.

→ Textbook 1A p16

Counting and writing numbers to 10

1 Count, then match each picture with its number.

five

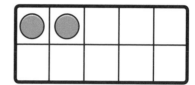

eight

3

7

2 Write how many balls there are in digits and in words.

There are ☐ ⚽ .

_____ ⚽

There are ☐ 🎾 .

_____ 🎾

There are ☐ 🏉 .

_____ 🏉

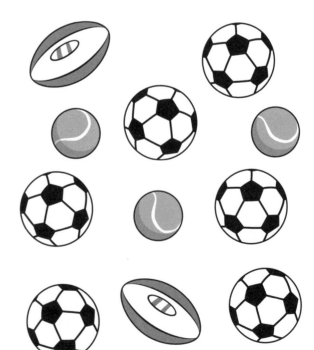

3 How many 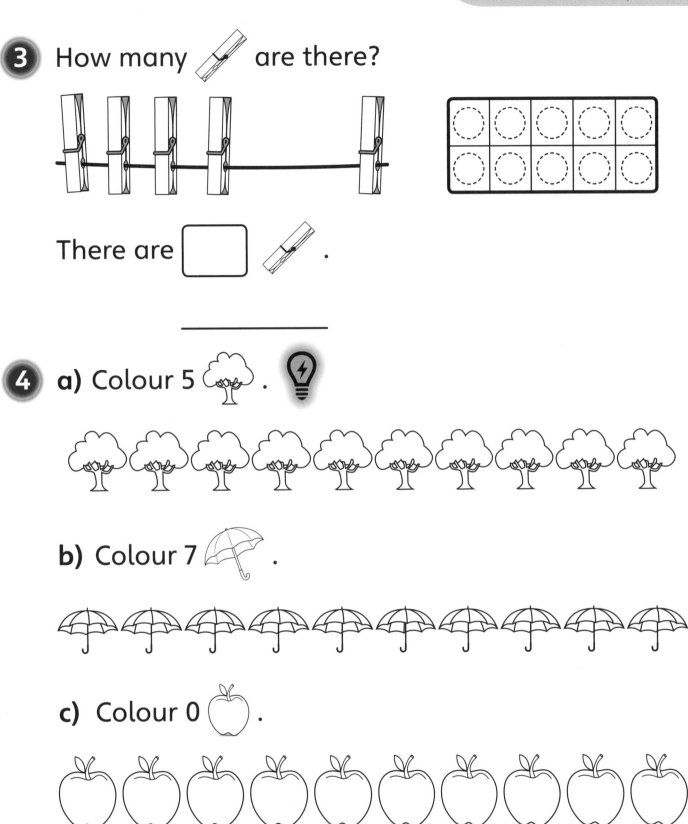 are there?

There are ☐ 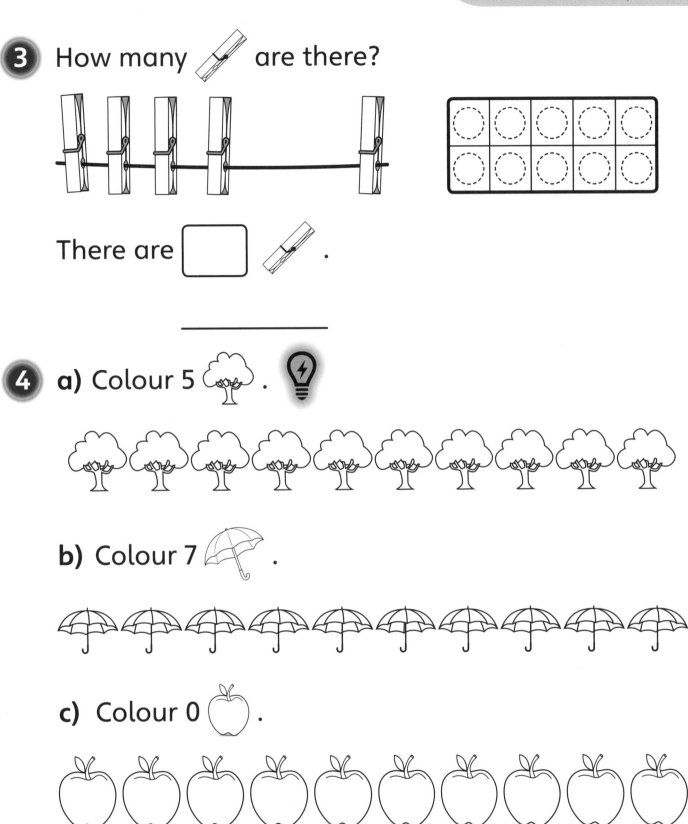 .

_____

4 **a)** Colour 5 🌳.

b) Colour 7 ☂ .

c) Colour 0 🍎 .

Did you colour the same as your friend?

5 How many 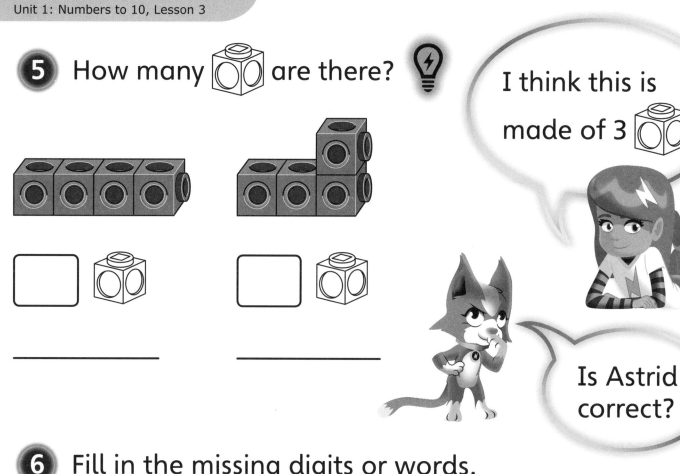 are there?

I think this is made of 3 🔲.

Is Astrid correct?

6 Fill in the missing digits or words.

1	2	3	4	___	___	___	___	9	10
one	___	three	four	___	six	seven	eight	___	___

Reflect

I will colour ▢ △ .

_____

Counting backwards from 10 to 0

 Fill in the number track.

a)

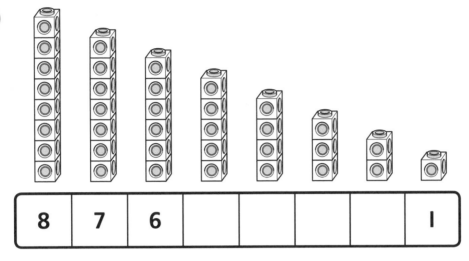

8	7	6						1

b)

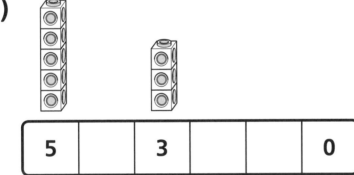

5		3			0

2 Fill in the number track.

a)

7	6		4	3			

b)

10		8		6	

c)

5				1

3 Emma counts from 6 to 0.

Complete what she says.

Six, five, _____, _____,

_____, _____, _____.

4 Fill in the missing numbers.

a)

		8	7	6

b)

				0

c)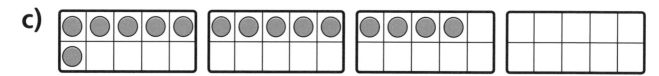

d)

6   7   8

e)

		3	4

I have noticed that some of these numbers go up.

5 Find the missing numbers.

CHALLENGE

```
        7
        
        5
1    3     5    7
        3
```

Reflect

Roll a 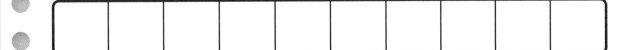.

What number did you roll? ☐

Count on to 10 from your dice number.

Count back to 0 from your dice number.

→ Textbook 1A p24

Counting one more

1 Fill in the numbers.

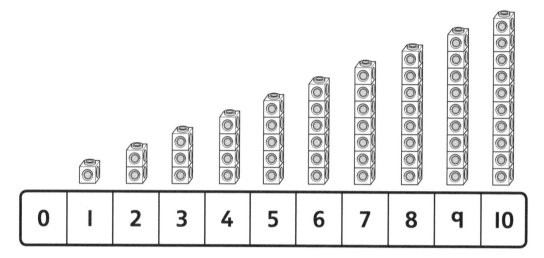

| 0 | 1 | 2 | 3 | 4 | 5 | 6 | 7 | 8 | 9 | 10 |

a) ⬚ is one more than 3.

b) 9 is one more than ⬚ .

c) One more than 7 is ⬚ .

2 Tay has 6 ✿ .

Lee has one more ✿ .

How many ✿ does Lee have?

Lee has ⬚ ✿ .

3 Fill in the missing numbers.

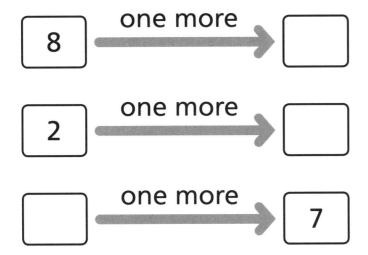

8	one more →	
2	one more →	
	one more →	7

4 Fill in the missing numbers.

CHALLENGE

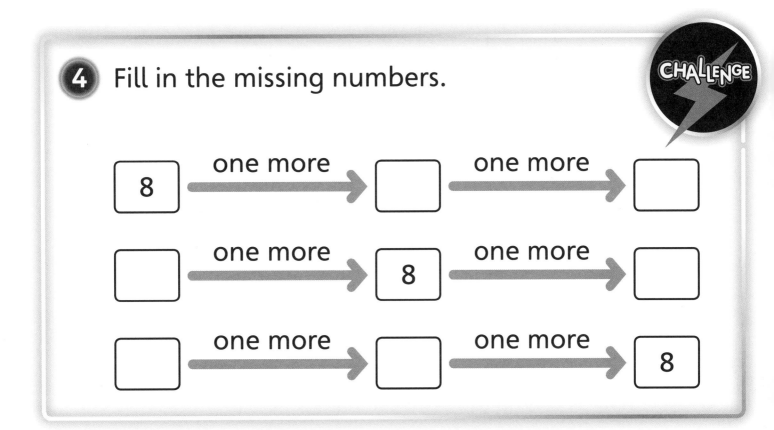

8	one more →		one more →	
	one more →	8	one more →	
	one more →		one more →	8

5 Show that 8 is one more than 7.

Show each number on the 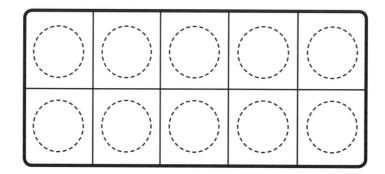.

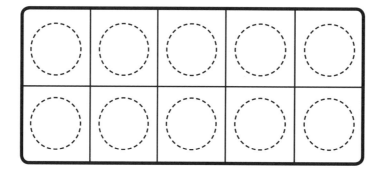

Reflect

I know that one more than ☐ is ☐.

☐ is one more than ☐.

I can use _____ to help me work out one more.

Counting one less

1 Fill in the numbers.

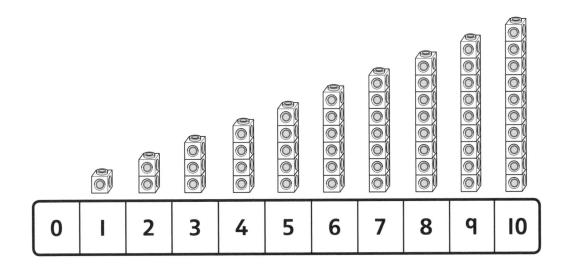

a) One less than 10 is ⬚.

One less than 1 is ⬚.

b) ⬚ is one less than 4.

⬚ is one less than 9.

c) ⬚ is one less than ⬚.

2 Juma has 5 . Lily has one less than Juma.

How many does Lily have?

Lily has ⬚ sweets.

3 Fill in the missing numbers.

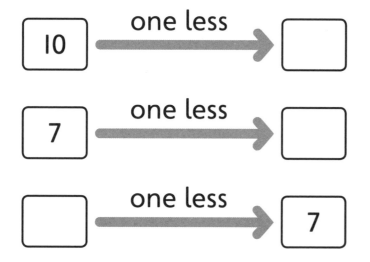

| 10 | one less → | ⬚ |

| 7 | one less → | ⬚ |

| ⬚ | one less → | 7 |

4 Complete the sentences.

a) 5 is _____ than 6.

b) 7 is _____ than 6.

5 Complete the table.

one less	number	one more
	8	
1		
		● ● ● ● ●

Show each number on the ⬚⬚⬚⬚⬚.

Reflect

Ask your friend to hold up some fingers.

Hold up one less than they do.

How many more fingers is your friend holding up?

→ Textbook 1A p32

Comparing groups

1 Are there more  or more ?

Tick the box.

2 Are there fewer or fewer children?

Tick the box.

children

3 Can each  have a  ?

Tick the box.

Yes ☐ No ☐

4 Complete the sentences.

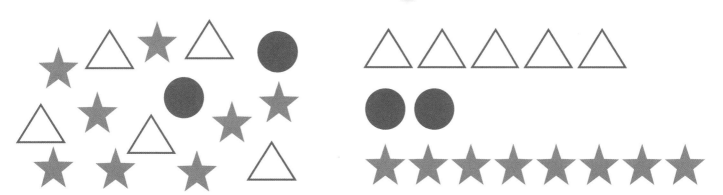

There are more △ than _____ .

There are _____ △ than ☆ .

There are 6 more ☆ than _____ .

Reflect

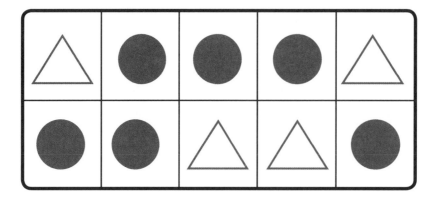

First I will count how many of each shape there are.

Look at the ☐☐☐☐☐.

Write a sentence using more or fewer.

- There are _____
- _____
- _____
- _____

Comparing numbers of objects

1 Complete the number sentences.

a)

7 ◯ 4

b)

4 ◯ 6

c)

☐ ◯ ☐

d)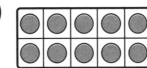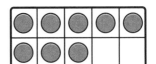

☐ ◯ ☐

2 Complete the number sentences.

a) There are more than because

5 ◯ 4.

b) There are fewer  than because

 < .

27

3 Complete the number sentences.

a)

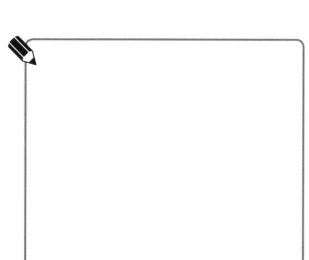

☐ ◯ ☐

b)

☐ ◯ ☐

4 Draw ▨ in the boxes to make the sentences correct. Then complete the sentences. 💡

a)

3 < ☐

b)

☐ = 5

5 Tim has  .

Lou has 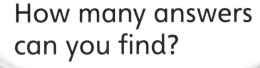 .

Anya has more than Tim and less than Lou.

How many could Anya have?

Anya could have ☐ .

How many answers can you find?

Reflect

  the number sentence that is correct.

 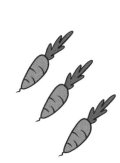

a) 4 < 3 ☐

b) 4 > 3 ☐

c) 4 = 3 ☐

Convince me!

→ Textbook 1A p40

Comparing numbers

1 Complete the number sentences.

a)

6 ◯ 8

b)

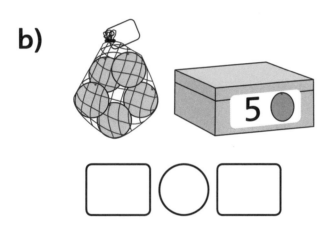

⬜ ◯ ⬜

c)

⬜ ◯ ⬜

2 Complete the number sentences.

a) 7 ◯ 7

b) 0 ◯ 4

c) 6 ◯ 5

d) 10 ◯ 2

e) 5 ◯ 6

f) 8 ◯ 3

3 Emma, Abha and Josh each have 2 number cards.
For each person circle the greatest number.

4 They each have two boxes of ⭐.

Circle the smaller number.

5 Complete these number sentences.

$\boxed{} < 6$

$10 > \boxed{}$

$5 < \boxed{}$

How many answers can you find for

$\boxed{} < 6?$

Reflect

Say a number.

The next person says a number that is greater.

The next person says a number that is smaller.

And so on.

Can the whole class do it?

32

Ordering objects and numbers

1 Circle the greatest.

a)

b)

c)

d)

e) **5** **8** **3**

f) **6** **0** **10**

2 Circle the least.

a)

b)

c)

d) **6** **8** **0**

e) four   eight   three

f)

3 Order the numbers.

a) 7, 8, 5   Start with the least.

☐ ☐ ☐

b) 3, 0, 1   Start with the greatest.

☐ ☐ ☐

c) 10, 1, 5, 9   Start with the least.

☐ ☐ ☐ ☐

d) five, six, ten   Start with the greatest.

_____ _____ _____ .

4 These number lists are in order.

Complete them.

a) 6, ☐ , 8

b) 9, 3, ☐

c) five, _____ , eight

d) ☐ , 7, 10

e) 7, ☐ , 4, ☐

5 Which tower has the most 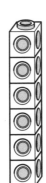 ?

Circle your answer.

CHALLENGE

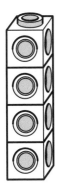 

Are they all the same?

Reflect

Put these numbers in order.

7   2   q

Explain your order.

35

→ Textbook 1A p48

First, second, third...

1 Label these pictures in the right order, from 1st to 4th.

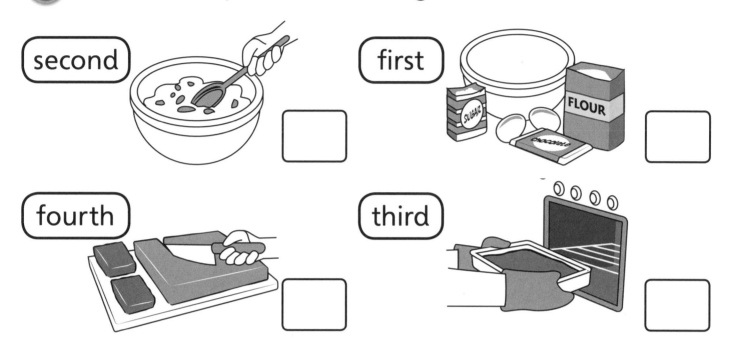

second

first

fourth

third

2 **a)** Colour the fourth ⃝ .

b) Circle the ninth 🦆 .

c) Circle all the 📖 before the 5th one.

3 Which is 3rd from the top,

the ⬛ or the ▯ ?

Which is 2nd from the bottom,

the ▯ or the △ ?

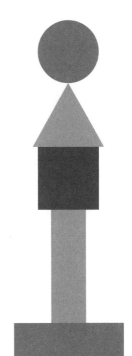

4 What is the code on Dan's  lock?

The 3rd digit is a 5.

The 2nd digit is one more than the first.

The Ist digit is the same as the fourth.

The 4th digit is a 7.

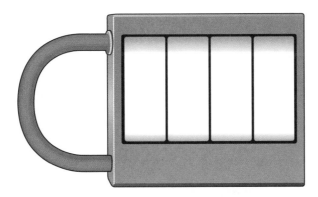

CHALLENGE

37

5 The 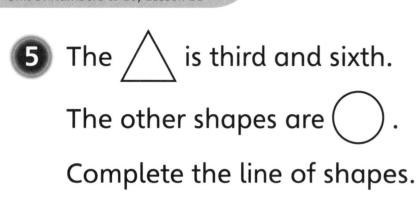 is third and sixth.

The other shapes are ◯.

Complete the line of shapes.

Reflect

Colour some ◯.

Ask a friend which ones you coloured (1st, 2nd, 3rd...).

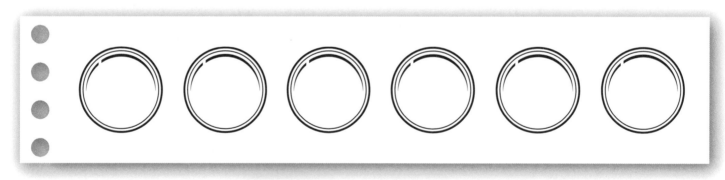

Are they right?

The number line

1 Complete the number lines.

a)

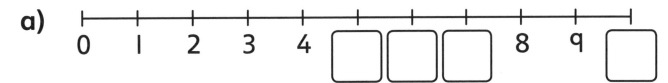

0 1 2 3 4 ☐ ☐ ☐ 8 9 ☐

b)

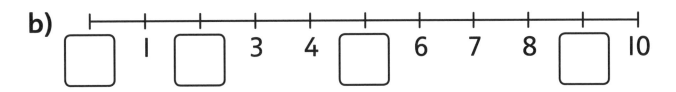

☐ 1 ☐ 3 4 ☐ 6 7 8 ☐ 10

c)

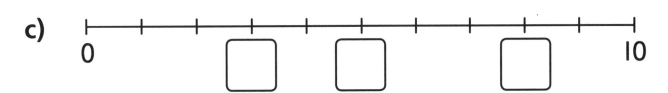

0   ☐   ☐   ☐   10

2 a) Draw an arrow to the number 7.

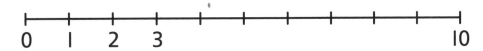

0 1 2 3   10

b) Draw an arrow to the number 2.

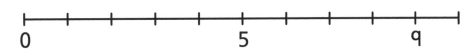

0   5   9

c) Draw an arrow to the number 7.

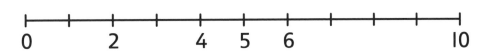

0   2   4 5 6   10

d) Draw an arrow to the number 6.

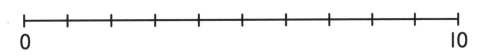

0   10

3 Use the number line to work out your answer and circle it.

a) Which is greater, 3 or 7?

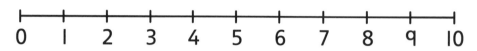

b) Which is greater, 10 or 2?

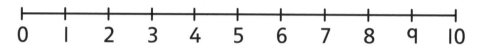

c) Which is less, 5 or 2?

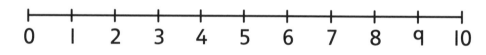

d) Which is the least, 6, 1 or 7?

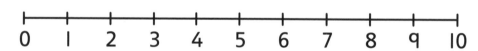

4 a) What is one more than 5?

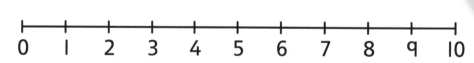

b) What is one less than 10?

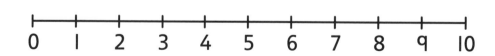

Show the jumps.

c) What is one less than 1?

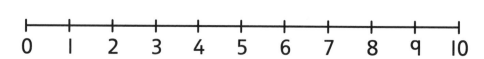

CHALLENGE

5 **a)** What is two more than 5? ☐

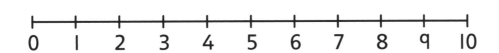

b) What is three less than 7? ☐

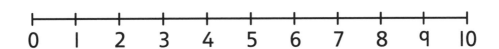

6 Use the number line to put 9, 5, 1 and 8 in order starting with the greatest.

☐ ☐ ☐ ☐

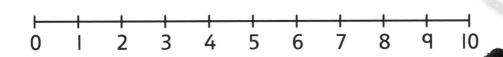

Let's circle the numbers on the line.

Reflect

I have learnt how to use a number line to _____

_____

_____

→ Textbook 1A p56

End of unit check

My journal

Bea has 5 red 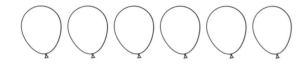 and I yellow ⬭. Colour them in.

⬭⬭⬭⬭⬭⬭

Seth has 3 red 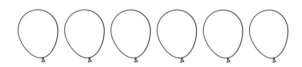 and 3 yellow ⬭. Colour them in.

⬭⬭⬭⬭⬭⬭

- What is the same? _____

- _____

- What is different? _____

- _____

These words might help you.

balloon   I   one

less   3   three

more   5   five

Power check

How do you feel about your work in this unit?

Power play

A game for 2 or more players.

You will need:
- 0 to 9 digit cards
-
-

How to play:
- Mix up the cards and put them face down on the table.
- Each player chooses a card.
- Make the number shown using the counters and the ten frame.
- The winner is the player with the largest number.

The part-whole model ❶

1 Complete the Y .

a)

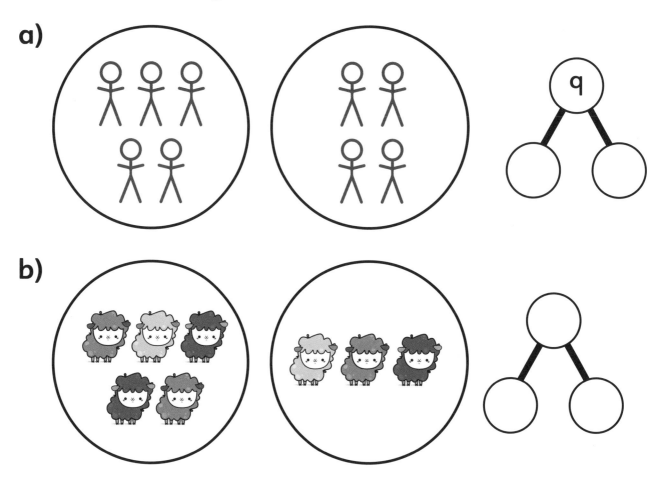

b)

2 Draw ▲ in the circles to show the two groups.

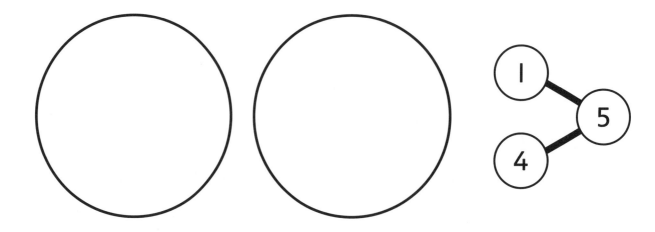

3 Match the circles to the .

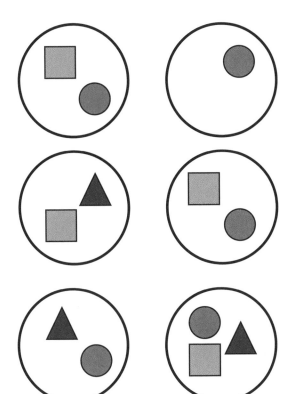

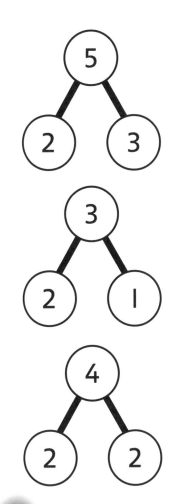

4 The are in different groups.

Complete each .

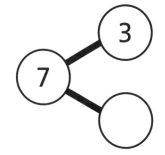

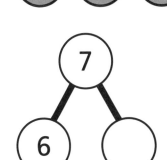

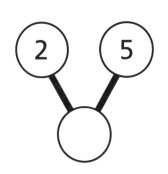

5 Sort the children into different groups.

Complete each .

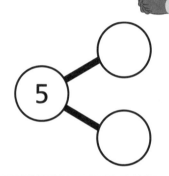

Can you group the children another way?

CHALLENGE

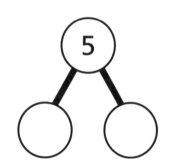 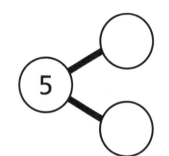 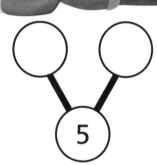 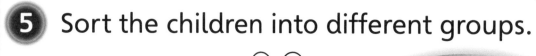

Reflect

Can you think of a  where the whole is not the biggest number?

True or false?

In a part-whole model, the whole is always the biggest number.

The part-whole model ❷

1 Draw the 2 groups of ✏. Fill in the 🍀.

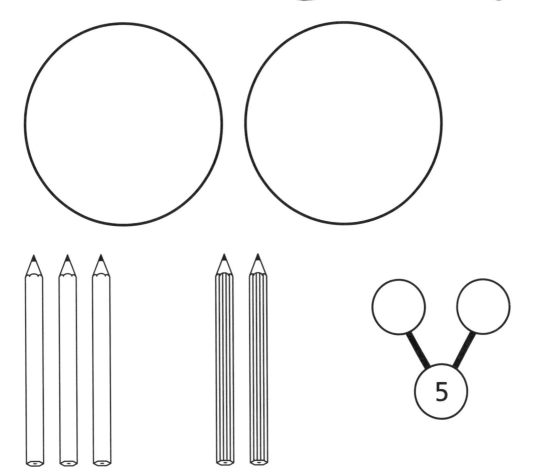

2 Match the number sentence to the 🍀.

$3 + 3 = 6$ $4 + 0 = 4$ $6 = 2 + 4$ $7 = 1 + 6$

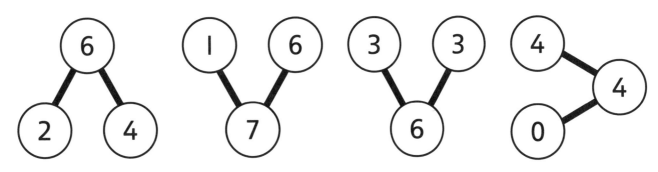

3 Complete the number sentences.

a)
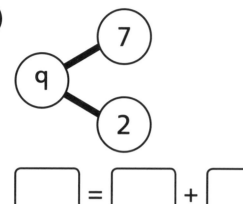

☐ = ☐ + ☐

b)
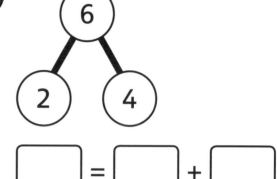

☐ = ☐ + ☐

4 Group the in different ways.

One has been done for you.

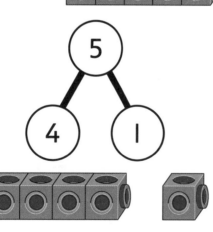

a)

c)
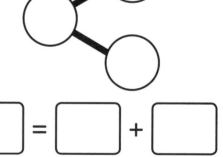

☐ = ☐ + ☐

b)
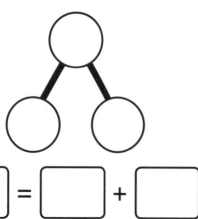

☐ = ☐ + ☐

d)
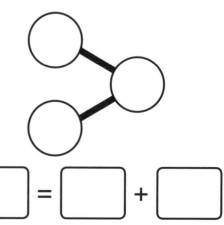

☐ = ☐ + ☐

5 How many different ways can you complete the 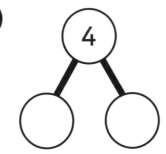?

a)

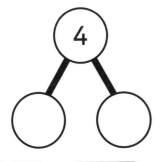

$\boxed{} + \boxed{} = 4$

c)

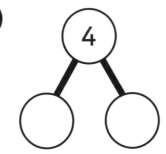

$\boxed{} + \boxed{} = 4$

e)

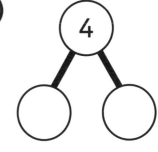

$\boxed{} + \boxed{} = 4$

b)

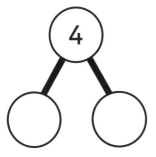

$\boxed{} + \boxed{} = 4$

d)

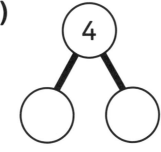

$\boxed{} + \boxed{} = 4$

I will use to help me.

Reflect

$8 = 3 + 5$ $8 = 5 + 3$

What is the same? What is different?

_____

_____

→ Textbook 1A p68

Related facts – number bonds

1 Complete the  and number sentences.

a) ⬚ + ⬚ = 8

b) 8 = ⬚ + ⬚

c) ⬚ + 5 = ⬚

d) ⬚ = 3 + ⬚

2 Look at the 🧺. Complete the 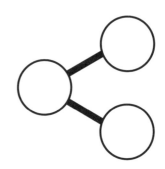 and number sentences.

a) 4 + ⬚ = 7

b) ⬚ = ⬚ + 3

c) ⬚ + 4 = ⬚

d) 7 = ⬚ + ⬚

3 Complete the number sentences.

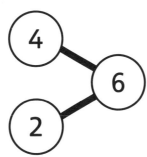

a) 4 + ☐ = 6

c) ☐ ◯ ☐ = 6

b) 6 = ☐ ◯ ☐

d) 6 = ☐ ◯ ☐

4 Look at the  . Complete the .

Write the number sentences.

I can make 4 number sentences from the picture.

Is Astrid correct?

_____

_____

_____

_____

5 Put the digits 5, 5 and 0 into the .
Then write the number sentences.

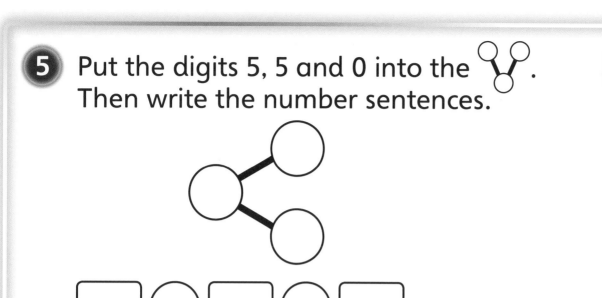

Reflect

Draw your own .

Ask your partner to write the number sentences to match.

Finding number bonds

1 Complete the  and the number sentences.

a) $4 = 1 +$ ☐

b) $4 = 2 +$ ☐

c) $4 =$ ☐ $+$ ☐

2 Complete the ☐☐☐☐☐ in the sequence.

Complete the number sentence.

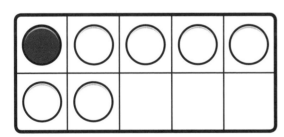

$1 + 6 = 7$

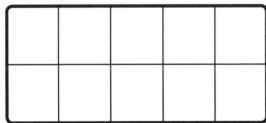

☐ $+$ ☐ $=$ ☐

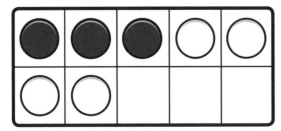

$3 + 4 = 7$

3 Circle the odd one out.

Explain your answer.

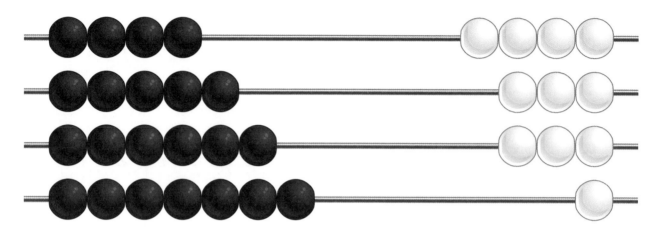

_____

_____

4 Find the value of ▲ and ●.

$▲ + 7 = 7$ $4 + 3 = 7$

$1 + 6 = 7$ $● + 2 = 7$

$2 + ● = 7$ $6 + 1 = 7$

$3 + 4 = 7$ $7 + ▲ = 7$

▲ = [ ]   ● = [ ]

5 Look at the ●●●●●——○○○○○ and the ▢▢▢▢▢ .

Aidan and Fleur are using them to write number sentences.

Aidan

Fleur

CHALLENGE

Who can write the most number sentences? Explain why.

_____

_____

Reflect

Draw 4 beads on each bead string to show the different ways of making 4.

→ Textbook 1A p76

Comparing number bonds

1 Who has more  ?

Circle the answer.

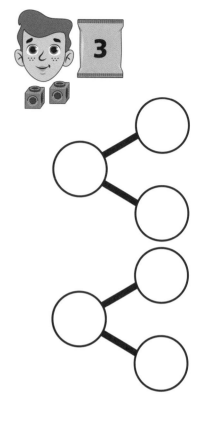

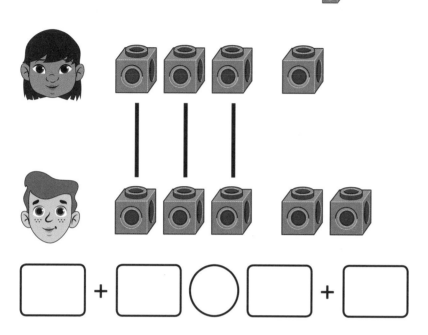

2 Who has more  ?

Circle the answer.

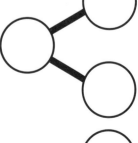

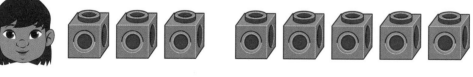

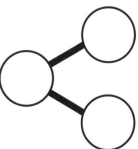

3 Replace $\bigcirc$ with <, > or =.

a) $3 + 5 \bigcirc 3 + 6$

b) $4 + 4 \bigcirc 5 + 4$

c) $1 + 6 \bigcirc 2 + 5$

d) $4 + 3 \bigcirc 7 + 1$

4 Choose a number to make each number sentence correct.

CHALLENGE

$2 + \boxed{} > 2 + 5$

$7 + 1 > 6 + \boxed{}$

$\boxed{} + 5 = 6 + 2$

5 What could each shape be worth?

▲ < 5

▲ + ▲ < ▲ + ●

● + ● = ■

▲ = ☐   ● = ☐   ■ = ☐

Reflect

Use any two of the cards to write a number sentence.

☐ + ☐ | 0 | 1 | 2 | 3 | 4 | 5 |

Compare your number sentence with a partner using <, > or =. Write the pair below.

End of unit check

My journal

Can you put nine of these numbers into the part-whole models?

1 2 3 4 5 6 7 8 9 10

  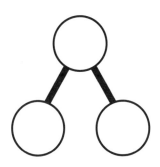

Is there more than one way?

These words might help you.

part

whole

is equal to

Power check

How do you feel about your work in this unit?

Power play

A game for 2 players.

> You will need:
> - counters
> - part-whole model

How to play:

- Choose a number between 5 and 10.
- This number is the whole. Put that many counters onto a part-whole model.
- Take it in turns to place 1 or 2 counters in one of the parts.
- If you make the whole, you win a point.
- If you don't make the whole, the next player goes.
- The first to 5 points is the winner.

Finding the whole – adding together

1 How many 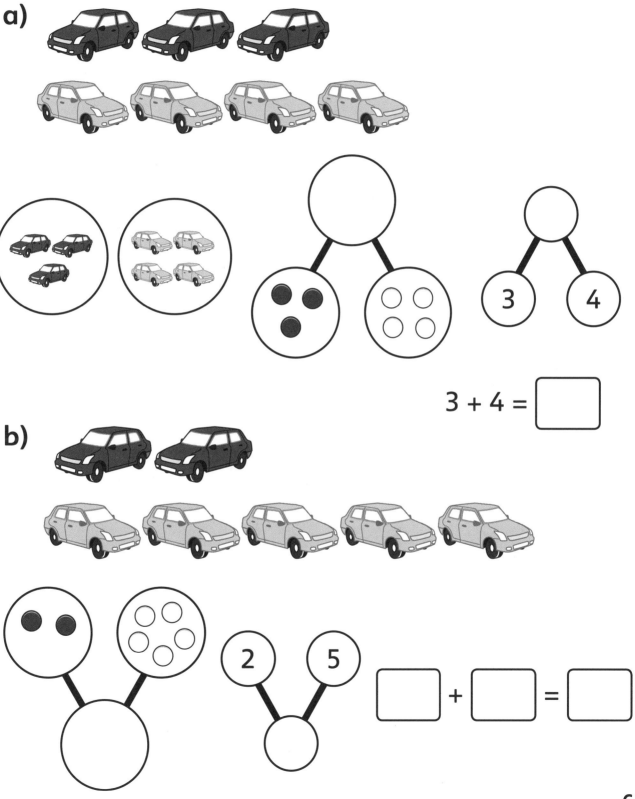 are there in total?

a)

$$3 + 4 = \boxed{}$$

b)

$$\boxed{} + \boxed{} = \boxed{}$$

2 How many  are there in total?

a)

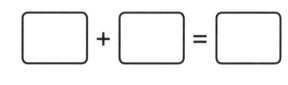

☐ + ☐ = ☐

b)

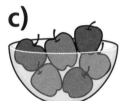

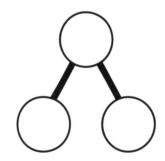

☐ + ☐ = ☐

c)

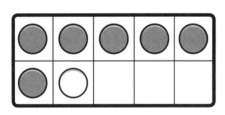

☐ + ☐ = ☐

3 Complete the and number sentences.

a)

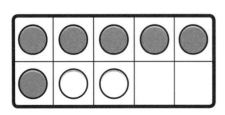

7 = ☐ + ☐

b)

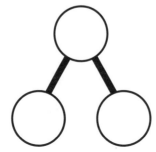

8 = ☐ + ☐

62

4 **a)** Complete the number sentences in two different ways.

□ + □ = 9   □ + □ = 9

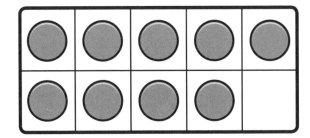   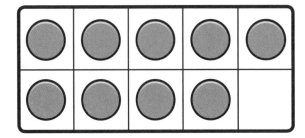

b) Complete the number sentence.

4 + 2 = □ + □

Reflect

I can find the total by _____

_____

Think about a and a ▯.

Finding the whole – adding more

1 How many fingers are held up in total?

a) 5 + ☐ = ☐

b) 5 + ☐ = ☐

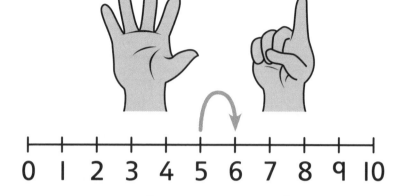

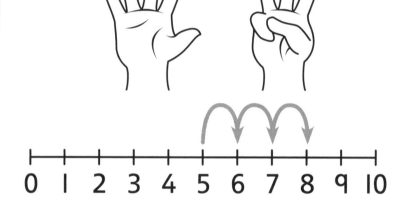

2 How many dots are there in total?

a) 4 + ☐ = ☐

b) 1 + ☐ = ☐

c) 5 + ☐ = ☐

d) 2 + ☐ = ☐

3 **a)** How many balls are there in total?

☐ + ☐ = ☐

There are ☐ balls in total.

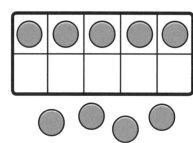

0 1 2 3 4 5 6 7 8 9 10

b) How many ◯ are there in total?

☐ + ☐ = ☐

There are ☐ ◯ in total.

0 1 2 3 4 5 6 7 8 9 10

4 Tom is working out how many ◯ there are in total. What mistake has he made?

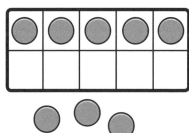

5, 6, 7   5 + 3 = 7

There are 7 ◯ in total.

5 **a)** 3 + 6 = ☐

0 1 2 3 4 5 6 7 8 9 10

b) 2 + 7 = ☐

0 1 2 3 4 5 6 7 8 9 10

c) ☐ = 5 + 3

0 1 2 3 4 5 6 7 8 9 10

d) ☐ = 6 + 4

0 1 2 3 4 5 6 7 8 9 10

6 Draw arrows to the number line.

One has been done for you.

2 + 3   1 + 0   5 + 4   4 + 6   3 + 3

0 1 2 3 4 5 6 7 8 9 10

Reflect

You can solve 2 + 8 = ☐ by _____

or by _____

Finding a part

1 There are 7 children in total.

How many children are in the 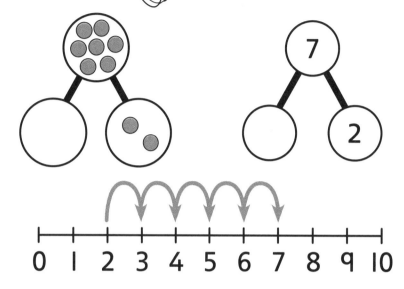 ?

$2 + \boxed{} = 7$

0 1 2 3 4 5 6 7 8 9 10

There are $\boxed{}$ children in the  .

2 9 people take a trip.

How many people are still on the 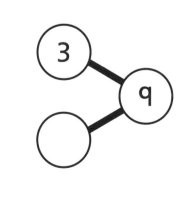 ?

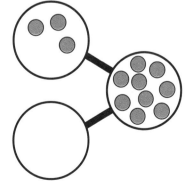

$3 + \boxed{} = 9$

There are $\boxed{}$ people still on the  .

3 Draw dice dots to make the total.

a)  + ☐ = 7

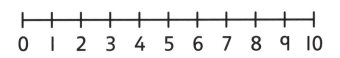

b) 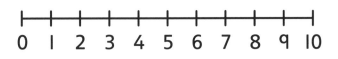 + ☐ = 7

c) ☐ + 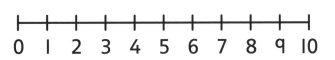 = 7

4 What mistake did I make?

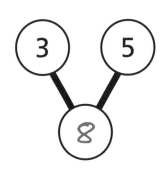

3 + 8 = 5

_____

_____

_____

5 Find the missing parts.

a) $1 + \boxed{} = 4$

You can use a number line to help you.

b) $\boxed{} + 3 = 7$

c) $9 = 8 + \boxed{}$

d) $3 + \boxed{} = 3$

0   1   2   3   4   5   6   7   8   9   10

6 Complete the number sentences.

CHALLENGE

$5 = 2 + \boxed{}$

$7 + \boxed{} = 9$

$5 = 3 + \boxed{}$

$7 + \boxed{} = 8$

$\boxed{} + 6 = 9$

$\boxed{} + 4 = 9$

Reflect

To work out $4 + \boxed{} = 7$, I could …

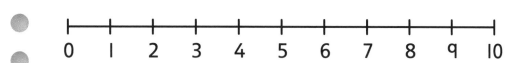

0   1   2   3   4   5   6   7   8   9   10

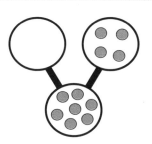

→ Textbook 1A p96

Finding and making number bonds

1 How many ducks are needed to make 10?

a) 4  + ☐ = 10

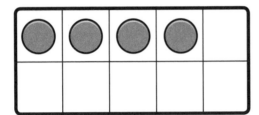

c) 7 + ☐ = 10

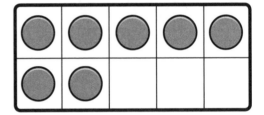

b) 6  + ☐ = 10

d) 3 + ☐ = 10

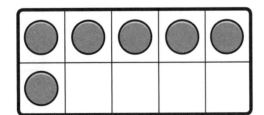

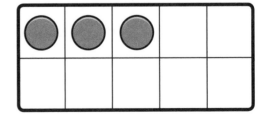

2 Find the missing part.

a) [   ] + 3 = 10

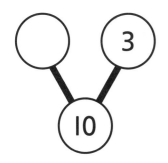 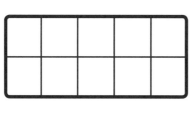

c) [   ] + 6 = 10

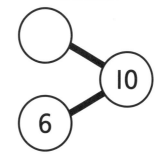 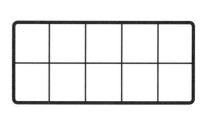

b) 5 + [   ] = 10

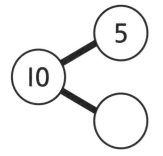 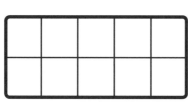

d) 9 + [   ] = 10

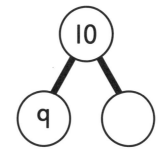 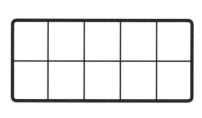

3 What do you add to 10 to make 10?

 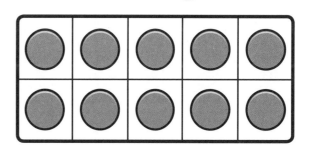

10 + [   ] = 10

CHALLENGE

4 What is each shape worth?

▲ + 5 = 7   ★ + 6 = 10

■ + ▲ = 10   ◆ + ★ = 9

■ = [ ]   ★ = [ ]

▲ = [ ]   ◆ = [ ]

Reflect

How many bonds to 10 can you find?

[ ] + [ ] = 10

Do your help?

Finding addition facts

1 How many children are there on each  ?

Find two ways to show each fact.

a) ☐ + ☐ = 10

☐ + ☐ = 10

b) ☐ + ☐ = 10

☐ + ☐ = 10

2 There are 10 , 10 and 10 .

Complete the additions.

a) ☐ + ☐ = 10   **b)** ☐ + ☐ = 10

c) ☐ + ☐ = 10

3 Join the pairs that add to make 10.

Do they all have a pair?

4 Complete the addition pairs.

a) $2 + \boxed{} = 10$

$\boxed{} + 2 = 10$

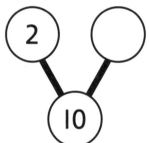

b) $10 = 3 + \boxed{}$

$10 = \boxed{} + 3$

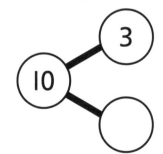

c) $10 = 9 + \boxed{}$

$\boxed{} + 9 = 10$

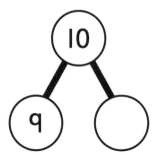

5 Use the cards to complete these additions.

☐ + ☐ = 10

3 + ☐ = 5

10 = 4 + ☐

| **2** | **3** | **6** | **7** | **8** |

6 What is the same? What is different?

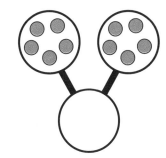

_____

_____

Reflect

I know that 6 + 4 = 10.

I also know that ☐ + ☐ = 10.

How many bonds to 10 do you know?

75

Solving word problems – addition

1 Complete and then match up.

a) How many 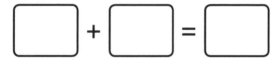 are there?

How many 🧣 are there?

How many 🎩 and 🧣 are there in total?

☐ + ☐ = ☐

b) How many children are sitting?

How many children are standing?

How many children are there altogether?

☐ + ☐ = ☐

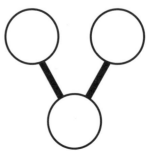

2 Here are some  .

2 more 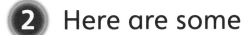 land.

a) How many are there in total?

☐ + 2 = ☐

0 1 2 3 4 5 6 7 8 9 10

There are ☐ 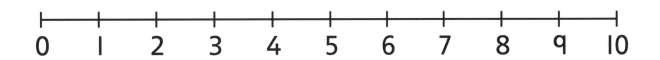 in total.

Here are some 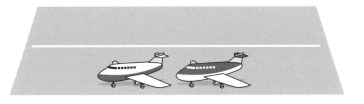 .

b) 6 more 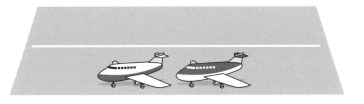 land.

How many 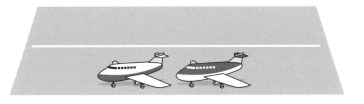 are there in total?

☐ + ☐ = ☐

0 1 2 3 4 5 6 7 8 9 10

There are ☐ 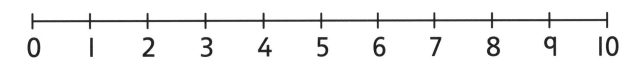 in total.

3 What are the scores?

Which score is greater?

CHALLENGE

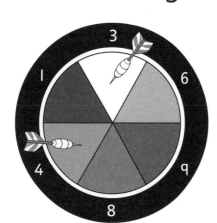

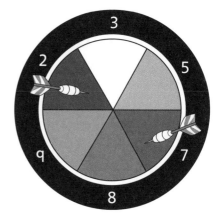

☐ + ☐ = ☐   ☐ + ☐ = ☐

☐ is greater than ☐.

Reflect

Draw  and to show 4 + 5 = ☐.

End of unit check

My journal

Choose an odd one out. Explain your choice.

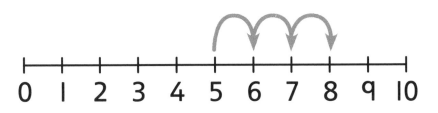

$$10 = 5 + 5$$

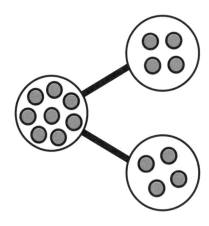

I chose it because _____

_____

_____ .

These words might help you.

part   **whole**

total

cube

add

number

Power check

How do you feel about your work in this unit?

Power play

A game for 2 players.

You will need:
- two different coloured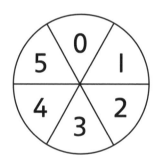
- | 1 | 2 | 3 | 4 | 5 | 6 | 7 | 8 | 9 | 10 |

How to play:
- Each player chooses two numbers from the target.
- Player 1 adds their two numbers and puts a ◯ on a number track to show the total.
- Player 2 adds their two numbers and puts a different coloured ◯ on a number track to show the total.
- Repeat. The ◯ must go on a different number each time.

Subtraction – how many are left? **1**

1 There are 6  in total.

2 melt.

How many are left?

There are ⬚ left.

2 There are 8 lit.

5 go out.

How many are still lit?

There are ⬚ still lit.

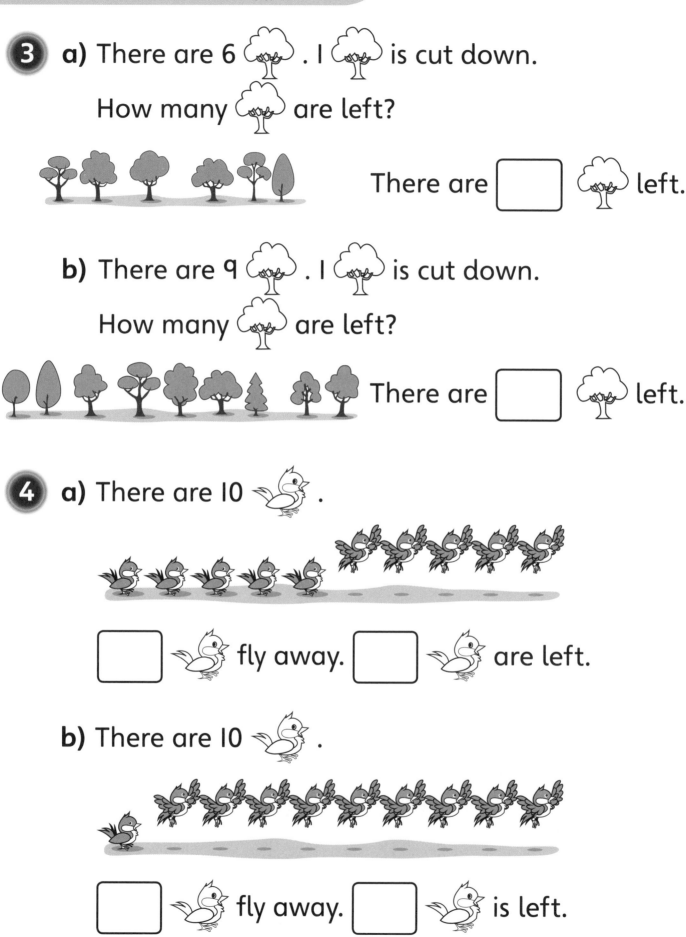

3 **a)** There are 6 🌳 . I 🌳 is cut down.

How many 🌳 are left?

There are ☐ 🌳 left.

b) There are 9 🌳 . I 🌳 is cut down.

How many 🌳 are left?

There are ☐ 🌳 left.

4 **a)** There are 10 🐦 .

☐ 🐦 fly away. ☐ 🐦 are left.

b) There are 10 🐦 .

☐ 🐦 fly away. ☐ 🐦 is left.

5 I have 7 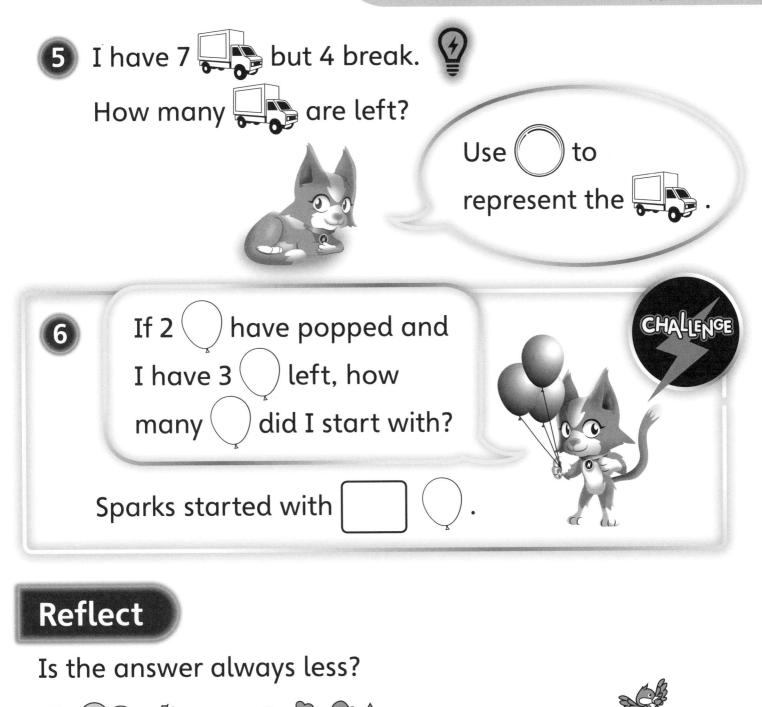 but 4 break.

How many are left?

Use ◯ to represent the.

6 If 2 ◯ have popped and I have 3 ◯ left, how many ◯ did I start with?

CHALLENGE

Sparks started with ▢ ◯.

Reflect

Is the answer always less?

I can work out how many are left by

→ Textbook 1A p116

Subtraction – how many are left?

1 There are 6  at the start.

2 ⬭ break.

How many ⬭ are left?

6 – ☐ = ☐

There are ☐ ⬭ left.

2 Complete each 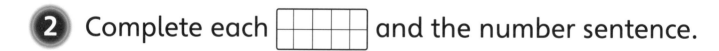 and the number sentence.

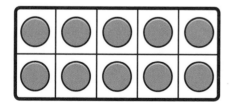 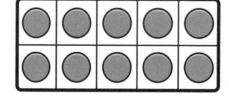 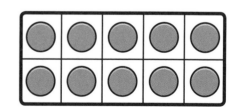

a) 10 – 1 = ☐

b) 10 – 5 = ☐

c) 10 – 7 = ☐

3 Complete the number sentences.

a) $8 - 3 =$ ☐

b) $6 - 5 =$ ☐

4 Complete the number sentences.

a)

☐ ◯ ☐ = ☐

b)

☐ ◯ ☐ = ☐

5 Complete each number sentence.

a)

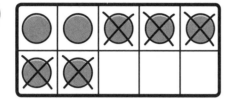

[ ] ◯ [ ] = [ ]

b)

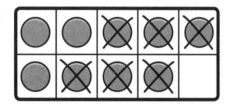

[ ] ◯ [ ] = [ ]

c)

○ ○ ○ ○

4 – 1 = [ ]

d)

8 – 4 = [ ]

e)

[ ]

7 – 5 = [ ]

f)

[ ]

4 – 4 = [ ]

Reflect

5 – 2 = 3 means _____

_____

_____

I can explain this with .

Subtraction – breaking apart ❶

1 There are 8 fish.

2 are .

How many are ?

8 – ☐ = ☐

There are ☐ .

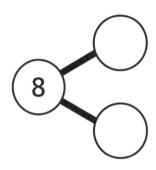

2 There are 10 pieces of fruit.

How many are 🍌 and

how many are 🍎 ?

☐ are 🍌 .

☐ – ☐ = ☐

There are ☐ 🍎 .

3 Complete the subtractions.

a)

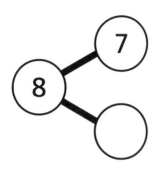

$8 - 7 = \boxed{}$

b)

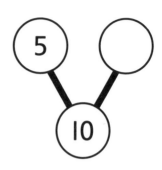

$10 - \boxed{} = \boxed{}$

4 3 belong to Tess.

How many belong to Mia?

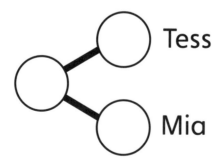 Tess

Mia

$\boxed{} - \boxed{} = \boxed{}$

5 What are the missing numbers?

a)

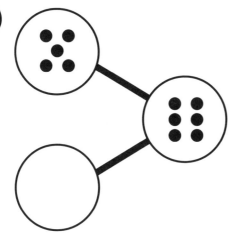

6 − 5 = ☐

b)

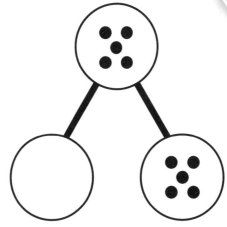

5 − 5 = ☐

Reflect

The whole is 8. One part is 5.

8 − 5 is ☐ because _____

_____

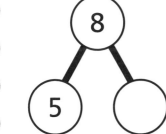
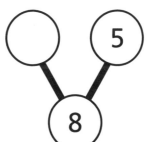
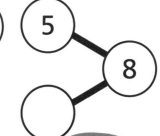

The diagrams change. Does the subtraction change?

89

→ Textbook 1A p124

Subtraction – breaking apart ❷

1 **a)** There are 9 animals in total.

There are 4 bigger animals.

How many smaller animals are there?

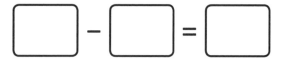

There are ☐ smaller animals.

b) There are 9 animals in total.

There are 6 bigger animals.

How many smaller animals are there?

There are ☐ smaller animals.

2 There are 9 in total. 4 are red, the rest

are white. How many are white?

There are ☐ white .

90

3 Complete the subtractions.

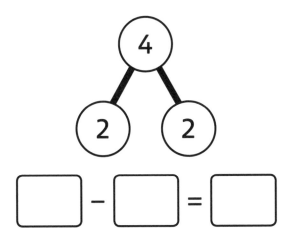

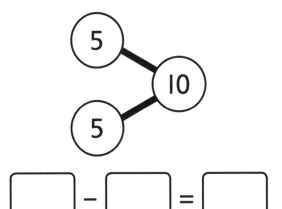

□ – □ = □   □ – □ = □

4 There are 8 pieces of fruit in total.

5 of these are .

How many  are there?

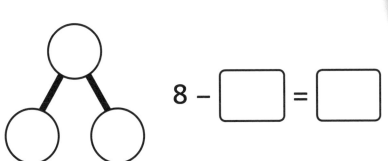

8 – □ = □

I can use ◯ to show the fruit.

There are □ .

5 Choose the cards that complete the subtractions.

1 | 3 | 7

a) 7 − 6 = ☐

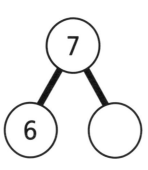

7 − 6 = ☐

b) 9 − 2 = ☐

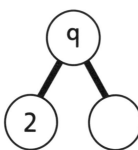

9 − 2 = ☐

I think there is a card I don't need!

Reflect

Explain the two mistakes.

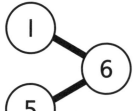

5 − 1 = ☐

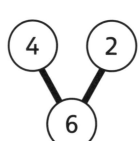

4 − 6 = ☐

Related facts – addition and subtraction ❶

1 There are $\boxed{}$ frogs in total.

$\boxed{}$ are on lily pads.

$\boxed{}$ are swimming.

Complete the number facts.

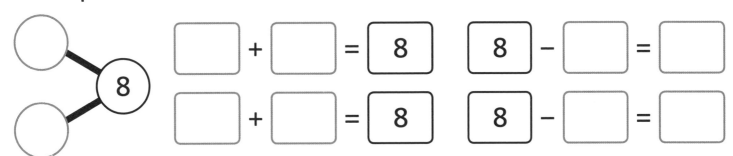

$\boxed{} + \boxed{} = \boxed{8}$ $\boxed{8} - \boxed{} = \boxed{}$

$\boxed{} + \boxed{} = \boxed{8}$ $\boxed{8} - \boxed{} = \boxed{}$

2 Use the picture to find four facts.

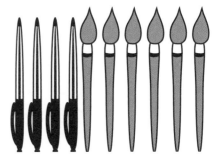

$\boxed{} + \boxed{} = \boxed{}$ $\boxed{} - \boxed{} = \boxed{}$

$\boxed{} + \boxed{} = \boxed{}$ $\boxed{} - \boxed{} = \boxed{}$

Which fact shows how many there are?

3 Find two more facts.

2 + 4 = 6   [ ] ◯ [ ] = [ ]

6 – 4 = 2   [ ] ◯ [ ] = [ ]

Circle the facts that tell you how many there are in total.

4 Use the picture to write four facts.

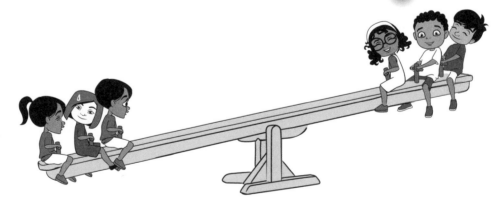

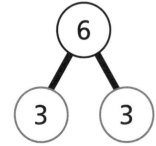

[ ] + [ ] = [ ]   [ ] – [ ] = [ ]

[ ] + [ ] = [ ]   [ ] – [ ] = [ ]

CHALLENGE

5 Match the question to the number sentence.

2 + 5 = 7

How many  are there?

7 – 5 = 2

How many horses are there in total?

7 – 2 = 5

How many are there?

Remember the whole and the parts.

Reflect

Circle the mistake.

4 + 5 = 9   5 – 9 = 4

5 + 4 = 9   9 – 4 = 5

I know this is the mistake because _____

_____

→ Textbook 1A p132

Related facts – addition and subtraction ❷

1 Here are some ducks.

Some ducks are . Some ducks are .

Fill in the and the number facts.

a)

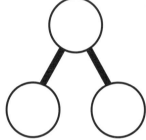

b) □ + 5 = 9   c) 9 = □ + □

2 Here are some frogs. Some are sitting.

One jumps away.

Fill in the number facts.

5 – 1 = □   5 – 4 = □

□ = 5 – 1   □ = 5 – 4

3 Complete the number sentences.

Join each question to the matching number sentence.

How many ⚲ are knocked down?

$4 +$ ☐ $= 10$

$10 = 4 +$ ☐

How many ⚲ are left up?

$10 - 4 =$ ☐

☐ $=$ ☐ $- 4$

How many ⚲ are there in total?

$4 =$ ☐ $-$ ☐

☐ $-$ ☐ $=$ ☐

4 Use the 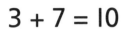 to fill in the number facts.

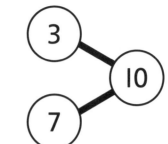

CHALLENGE

3 + 7 = 10

◻ ◯ ◻ = ◻   ◻ ◯ ◻ = ◻

◻ = ◻ ◯ ◻   ◻ = ◻ ◯ ◻

◻ = ◻ ◯ ◻   ◻ = ◻ ◯ ◻

5 Can you complete 4 different number sentences?

◻ – ◻ = ◻   ◻ = ◻ – ◻

◻ – ◻ = ◻   ◻ = ◻ – ◻

Reflect

If I know 6 – 4 = 2, I also know that _____

_____

_____

Subtraction – counting back

1 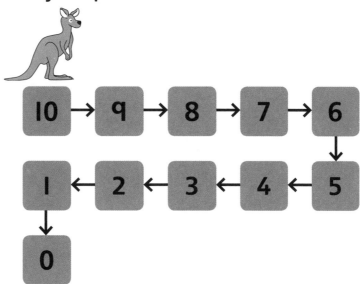 makes 6 jumps. Where does he land?

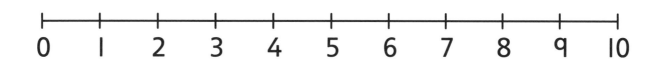

0   1   2   3   4   5   6   7   8   9   10

2 Fill in the number facts. Match the number line to the subtraction.

10 – 6 = ▢

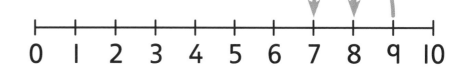

9 – 2 = ▢

▢ = 10 – 4

99

3 How far does  jump to catch ?

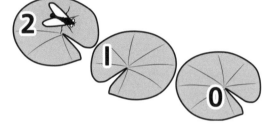

$7 - \boxed{} = 2$

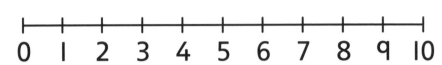

0 1 2 3 4 5 6 7 8 9 10

 makes $\boxed{}$ jumps.

4 $8 - 3 = \boxed{}$

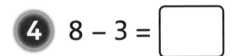

0 1 2 3 4 5 6 7 8 9 10

$6 - \boxed{} = 4$

0 1 2 3 4 5 6 7 8 9 10

$\boxed{} - 1 = 8$

0 1 2 3 4 5 6 7 8 9 10

$\boxed{} - 6 = 0$

0 1 2 3 4 5 6 7 8 9 10

5 Complete 5 different subtractions.

All should have the answer 5.

The first one has been done for you.

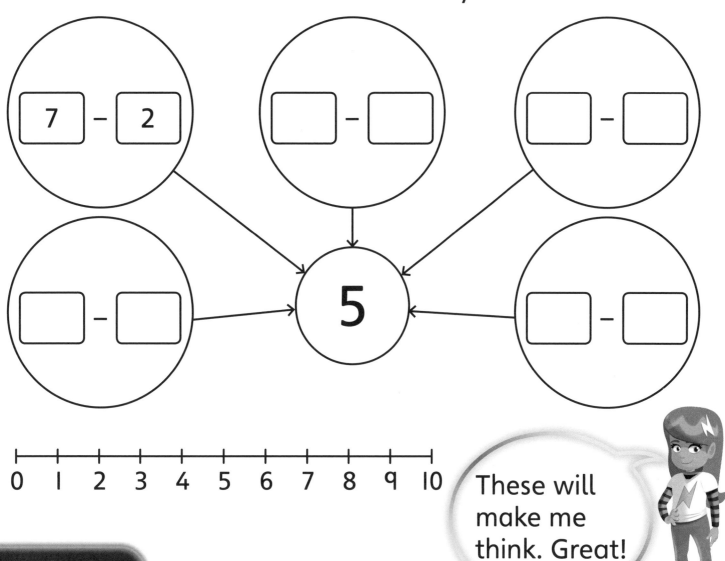

These will make me think. Great!

Reflect

There are lots of ways to subtract.

- I could _____
- _____
- _____

Subtraction – finding the difference

1 How many more 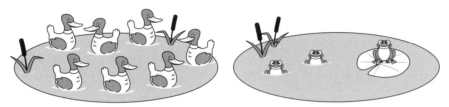 than ?

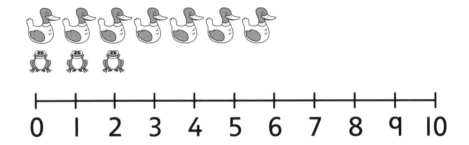

$$\boxed{} - \boxed{} = \boxed{}$$

There are $\boxed{}$ more  than .

2 How many fewer ?

a)

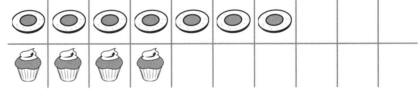

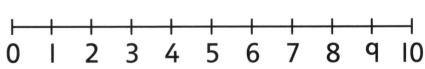

$$\boxed{} - \boxed{} = \boxed{}$$ There are $\boxed{}$ fewer  .

b)

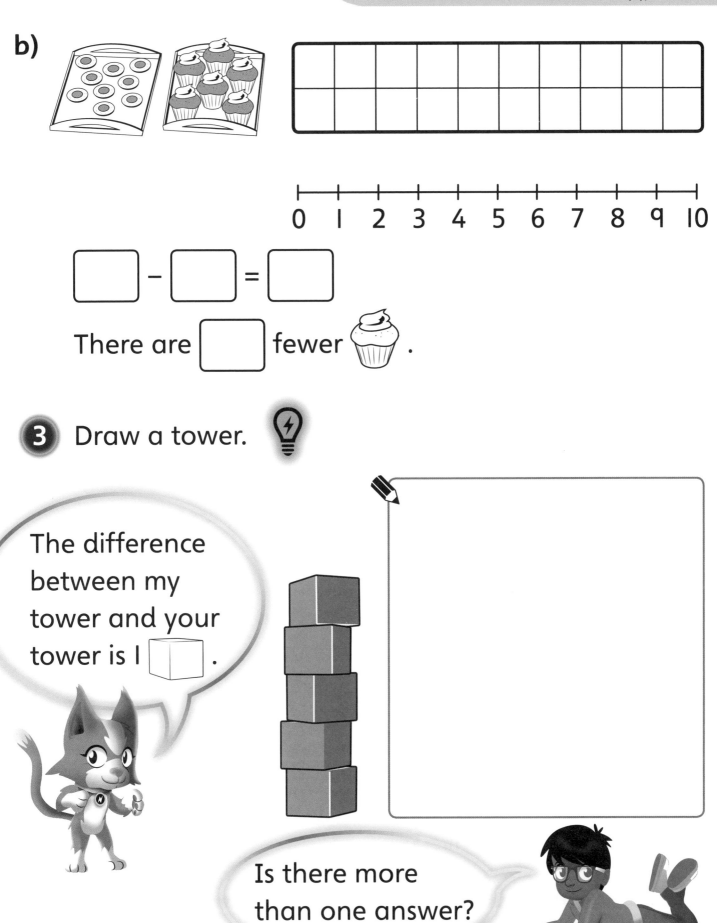

0 1 2 3 4 5 6 7 8 9 10

☐ – ☐ = ☐

There are ☐ fewer 🧁 .

3 Draw a tower.

The difference between my tower and your tower is 1 ☐ .

Is there more than one answer?

4 Pick a card to complete each sentence.

CHALLENGE

| 8 | 0 | 5 | 3 | 9 |

7 is 2 less than ▢.

▢ is 5 more than 3.

The difference between 9 and 6 is ▢.

8 is ▢ more than 8.

Reflect

There are ▢ birds on one branch.

There are ▢ birds on the other branch.

What is the difference?

▢ – ▢ = ▢

2 more birds arrive.

The difference stays the same. Draw the birds.

Solving word problems – subtraction

1 **a)** A spider has 8 legs. 2 legs have socks.

How many legs do not have socks?

8 – ☐ = ☐

☐ legs do not have socks.

b) There are ☐  .

There are ☐  .

How many more 🐌 than 🐌 ?

☐ – ☐ = ☐

2 Match the calculation with the question.

8 – 2 = 6   How many need  ?

8 – 3 = 5   How many need 🎩 ?

a) Complete the subtraction stories.

There are ☐ children in total.

☐ have .   ☐ – ☐ = ☐

☐ have ⌒.   ☐ – ☐ = ☐

There are ☐ children in total.

☐ wear 👓.   ☐ – ☐ = ☐

There are ☐ children with 👓.

b) Make up your own number story.

There are ☐ more ☐ than ☐.

4 Complete the subtraction story

for 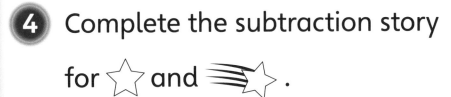 and .

How many more [ ] than [ ] ?

[ ] ◯ [ ] ◯ [ ]

There are [ ] more [ ] than [ ] .

We need to make up the question.

Reflect

$10 - 2 = 8$

Write a story for this subtraction.

- The 10 means _____
- The − 2 means _____
- The 8 means _____

→ Textbook 1A p148

Comparing additions and subtractions ❶

❶ There are 6 children.

There are 5 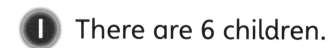 in the shed and

2 more  outside.

Shed   Outside

a) How many bikes are there in total?

5 + 2 = ☐

There are ☐ bikes in total.

b) Can all the children have a bike?

☐ > ☐

Yes ☐   No ☐

2 Use <, > and = to complete the number sentences.

a)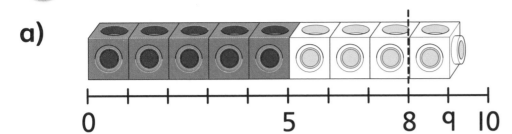

5 + 4 ◯ 8

b)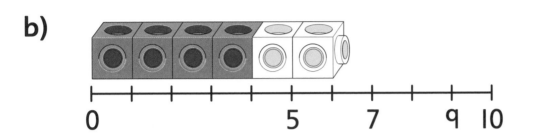

4 + 2 ◯ 7

c)

7 − 2 ◯ 3

3 Use <, > and = to complete the number sentences.

a) 3 + 4 ◯ 5

5 + 1 ◯ 4

2 + 6 ◯ 9

6 ◯ 1 + 5

b) 4 − 3 ◯ 3

5 − 2 ◯ 3

4 ◯ 6 − 1

8 − 2 ◯ 5

4 Draw lines to match each calculation to more than 5 or less than 5.

$3 + 5$ $1 + 2$ $2 + 2$ $6 - 2$

$2 + 5$ **< 5** **> 5** $6 - 3$

$9 - 5$ $9 - 3$ $9 - 1$

5 Which number statement is true?

Use the diagram to prove it.

$4 + 3 < 6$ $4 + 3 > 6$ $4 + 3 = 6$

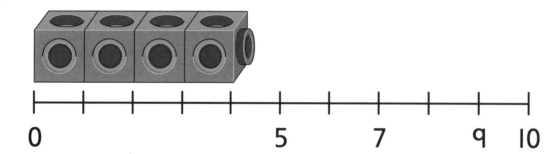

0   5   7   9   10

Reflect

Which symbols should I use?

$2 + 4 \bigcirc 7$ $4 + 4 \bigcirc 7$ $7 \bigcirc 9 - 4$

Comparing additions and subtractions ❷

1 **a)** Use >, < or = to complete the number sentence.

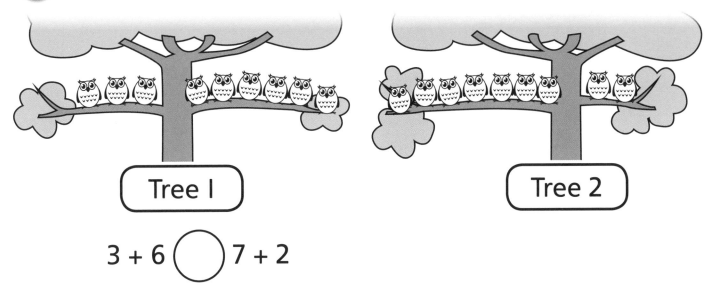

Tree 1   Tree 2

3 + 6 ◯ 7 + 2

b) Which tree has more owls? Tick the answer.

Tree 1 ☐   Tree 2 ☐   They are equal ☐

2 Complete the number sentences.

a)   4 + 4 ◯ 2 + 7

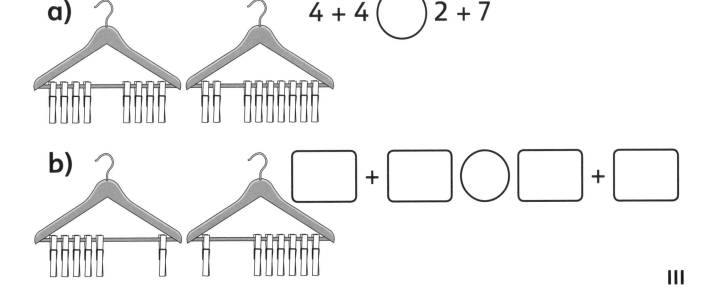

b)   ☐ + ☐ ◯ ☐ + ☐

III

3 Use <, > or = to complete the number sentences.

a)

$4 + 2 \bigcirc 3 + 2$

b)

$5 + 1 \bigcirc 3 + 3$

c)

$6 - 3 \bigcirc 6 - 2$

4 Use <, > or = to complete the number sentences.

a) $7 + 5 \bigcirc 5 + 7$

$4 + 5 \bigcirc 4 + 3$

$3 + 1 \bigcirc 3 + 3$

b) $8 - 3 \bigcirc 8 - 4$

$5 - 3 \bigcirc 4 - 3$

$3 - 3 \bigcirc 4 - 4$

5 Complete each number sentence.

CHALLENGE

$5 - 2 > \boxed{} + \boxed{}$

$5 - 3 > \boxed{} + \boxed{}$

$\boxed{} + \boxed{} > 10 - 1$

$\boxed{} + \boxed{} < 10 - 8$

Reflect

Make number sentences using the numbers **2**, **3**, **4**, **5**.

Ask a friend to check your number sentences.

→ Textbook 1A p156

Solving word problems – addition and subtraction

1 Hamsa has 8  .

Lucy has 5 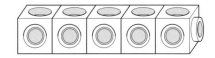 .

How many more  does Hamsa have?

2 a) There are 3 in the cup.

Hamsa puts 5 more  in the cup.

3 + ☐ = ☐

There are ☐  in the cup.

b) Lucy takes out 6 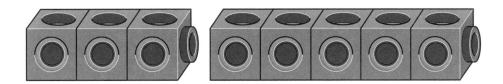 from the cup.

$$\boxed{} - 6 = \boxed{}$$

There are $\boxed{}$ in the cup.

3 Match and complete.

3 + 2 = $\boxed{}$

8 − 3 = $\boxed{}$

$\boxed{}$ = 5 + 3

$\boxed{}$ = 7 − 3

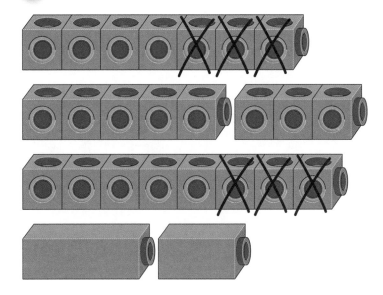

4  + = 10

 + ▲ = 8

▲ − ⬤ = 1

What number does each shape represent?

 = ☐

▲ = ☐

⬤ = ☐

 CHALLENGE

Reflect

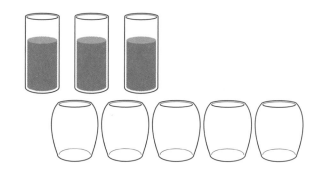

Use the picture to write your own maths question.

- _____
- _____
- _____

End of unit check

My journal

Iris says she can see two facts.

$6 = 3 + 3$ $3 + 3 = 6$

Marc says he can see three facts.

$6 - 3 = 3$ $3 - 6 = 3$ $3 = 6 - 3$

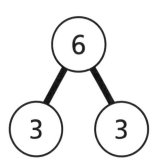

Explain the mistake that Marc has made.

The mistake is _____

because _____

_____ .

These words might help you.

part   add

whole

subtract   equals

take away

Power check

How do you feel about your work in this unit?

Power puzzle

| 0 | 1 | 2 | 3 | 4 | 5 |

Can you use all six cards to make both of these number sentences true?

We all need practice to get this right!

Can you find a different way?

Naming 3D shapes ❶

❶ Join the pairs of shapes.

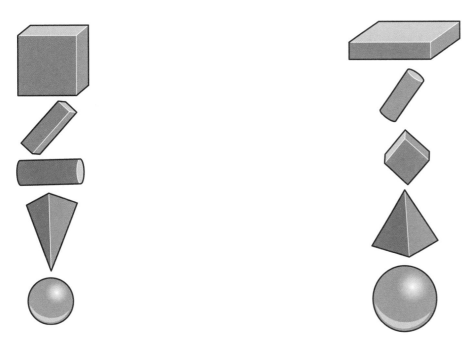

2 Circle the odd one out.

a)

b)

c)

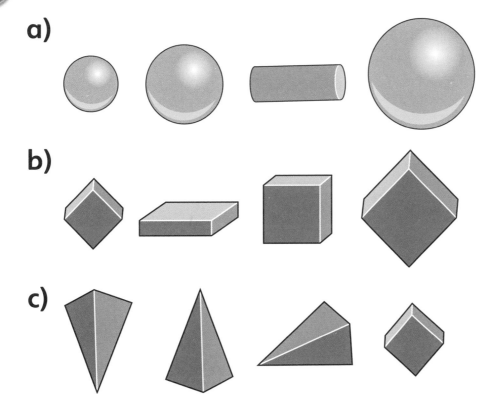

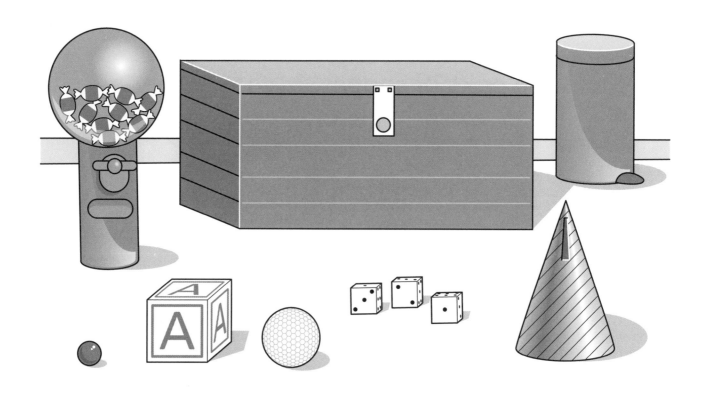

3 **a)** How many 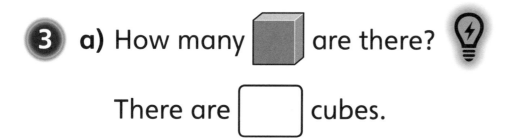 are there?

There are ☐ cubes.

b) How many ⬤ are there?

There are ☐ spheres.

c) How many ⬭ are there?

There are ☐ cylinders.

4 Name the hidden shapes.

CHALLENGE

| sphere | pyramid | cube | cuboid |

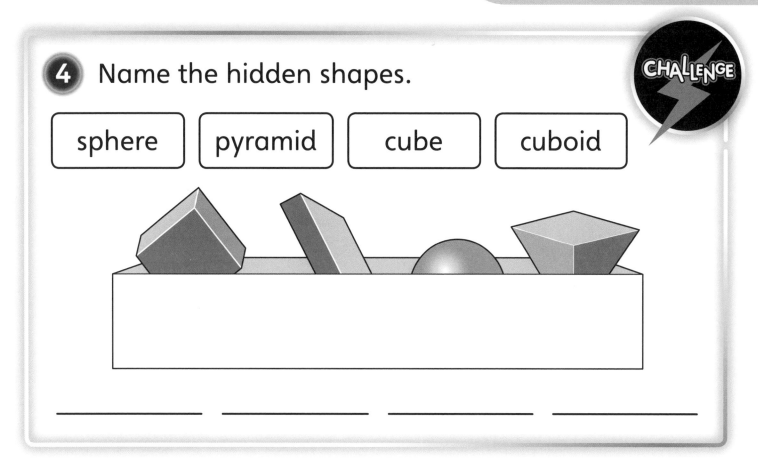

_____ _____ _____ _____

Reflect

Where can you find different shapes at school or at home?

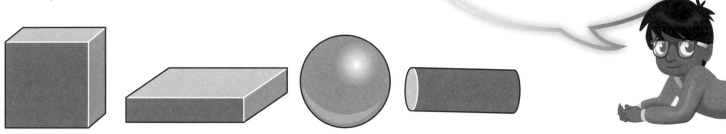

Where would you find a △ ?

→ Textbook 1A p168

Naming 3D shapes ❷

1 Match each shape to its name.

cube

sphere

cylinder

pyramid

cuboid

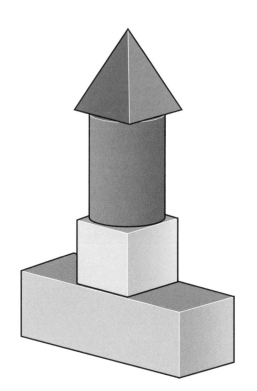

2 Circle the cuboids.

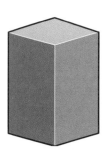

3 ✔ the true sentences.

Adele used more cubes. ☐

Hiro used fewer pyramids. ☐

Both used one cylinder. ☐

They used some spheres. ☐

Adele   Hiro

4 Match the boxes to the objects. 💡

2 spheres
I cone
I cuboid

I cuboid
I pyramid
2 cylinders

I cube
I cuboid
I cylinder
I sphere

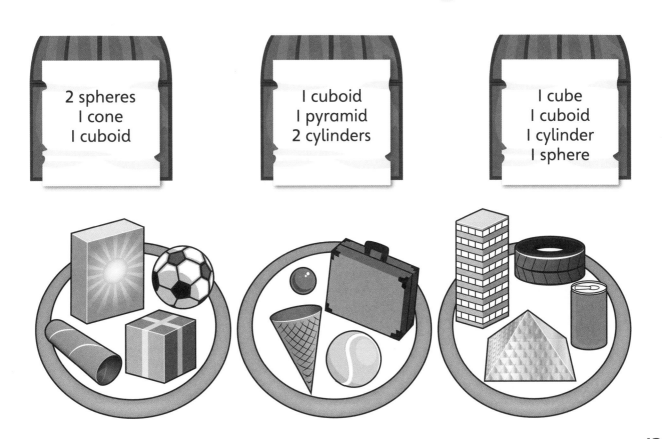

5 Write the correct letter in each hoop.

CHALLENGE

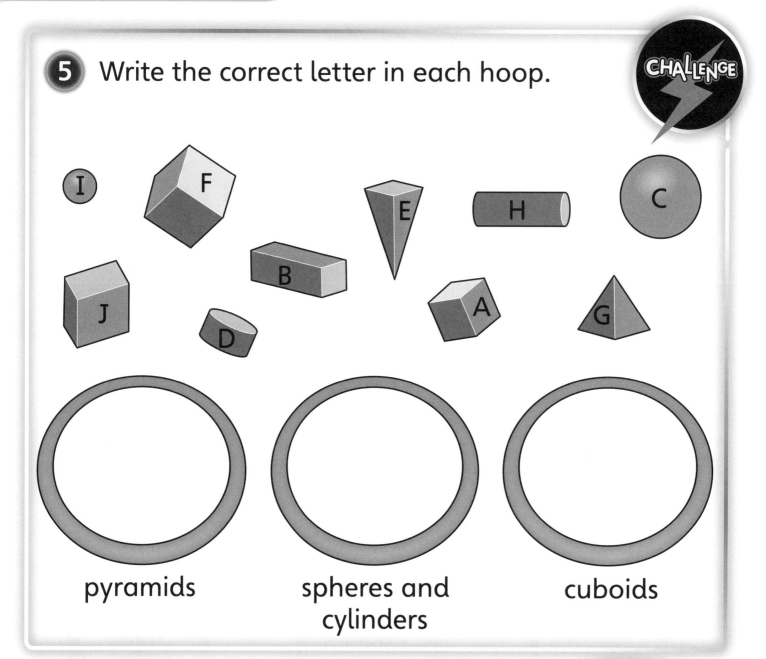

pyramids

spheres and cylinders

cuboids

Reflect

Can you name 5 different 3D shapes?

Can you see each shape in the classroom?

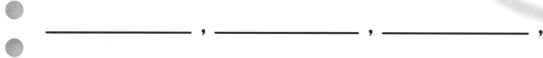

_____ , _____ , _____ ,

_____ , _____ .

Naming 2D shapes ①

① Match each shape to the correct name.

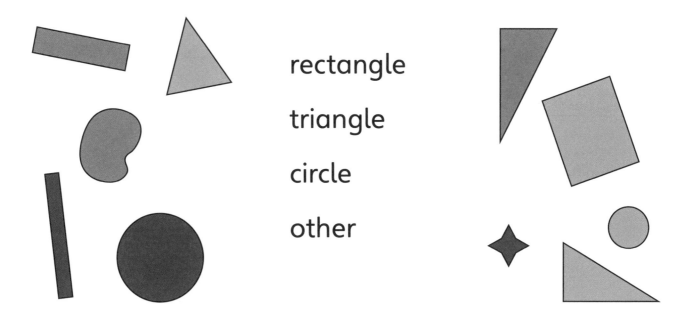

rectangle

triangle

circle

other

② Circle the odd one out.

a)

c)

b)

d)

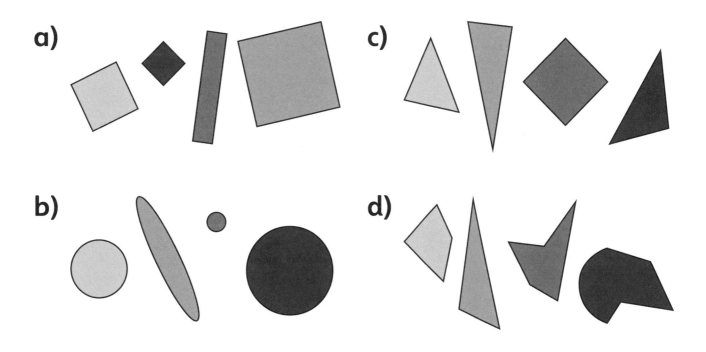

3 Name the shapes.

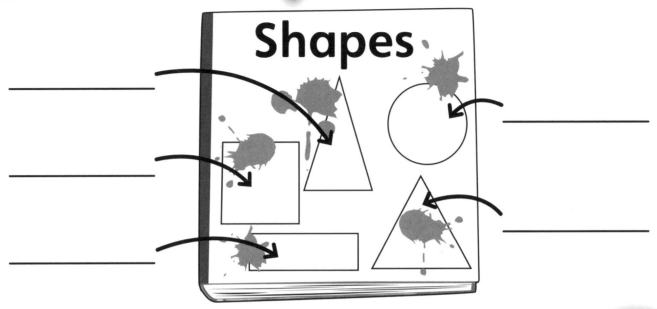

_____

_____

_____

_____

_____

4 Can you make a rectangle using 6 squares?

5 Colour and count the shapes.

CHALLENGE

blue = rectangles

yellow = triangles

red = circles

a) There are ☐ circles.

b) There are ☐ rectangles.

c) There are ☐ triangles.

Reflect

Name the different shapes.

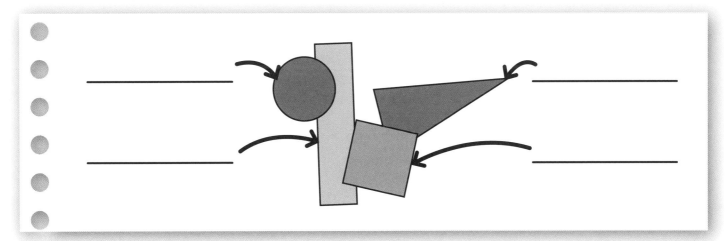

_____   _____

_____   _____

→ Textbook 1A p176

Naming 2D shapes ❷

① Join the 3D shapes to the 2D shapes they print.
Use the words to complete the sentences.

circle

square

rectangle

triangle

a) The cube prints a _____ .

b) The cuboid prints a _____ .

c) The pyramid prints a _____ .

d) The cone prints a _____ .

② Cross out the print the 3D shape cannot make.

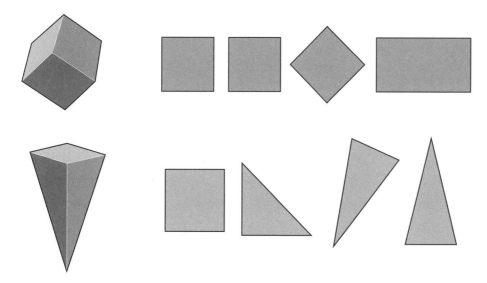

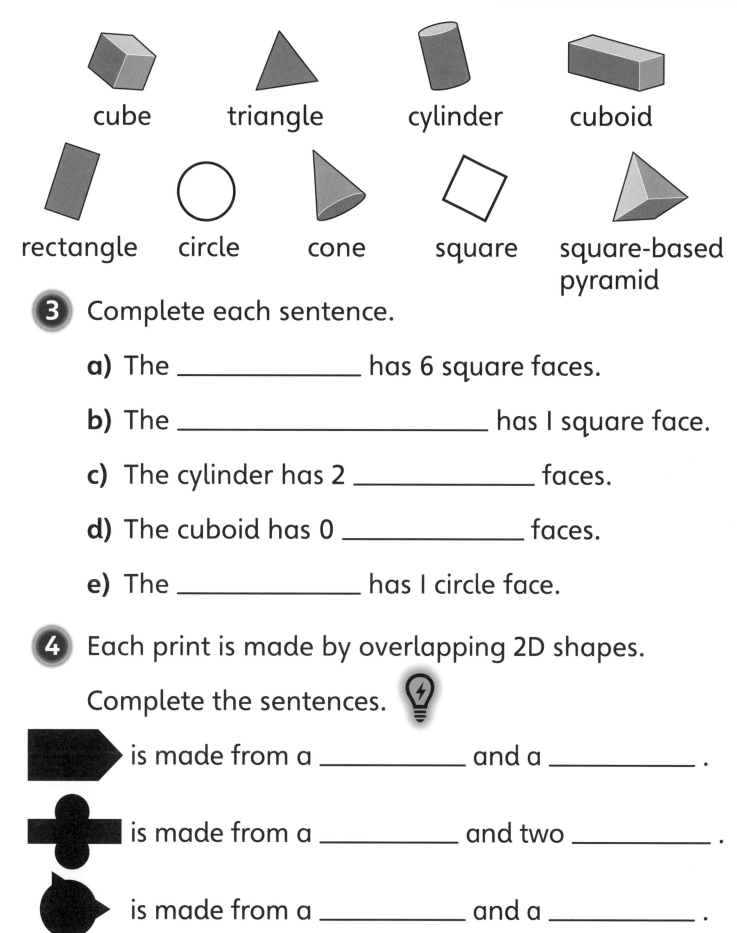

cube   triangle   cylinder   cuboid

rectangle   circle   cone   square   square-based pyramid

3 Complete each sentence.

a) The _____ has 6 square faces.

b) The _____ has I square face.

c) The cylinder has 2 _____ faces.

d) The cuboid has 0 _____ faces.

e) The _____ has I circle face.

4 Each print is made by overlapping 2D shapes.

Complete the sentences.

is made from a _____ and a _____ .

is made from a _____ and two _____ .

is made from a _____ and a _____ .

129

5 Match the shape with when it was printed. **CHALLENGE**
Some were printed twice.

first

rectangle

second

square   third

triangle   fourth

fifth

circle

sixth

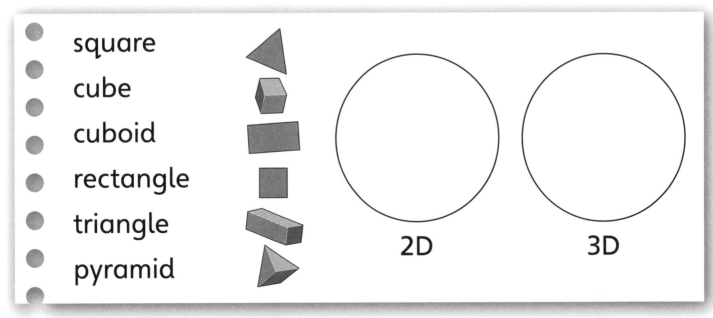

Reflect

Match the name and the shape. Write the correct
names in each circle.

- square
- cube
- cuboid
- rectangle
- triangle
- pyramid

2D   3D

Making patterns with shapes

1 Continue each pattern.

a)

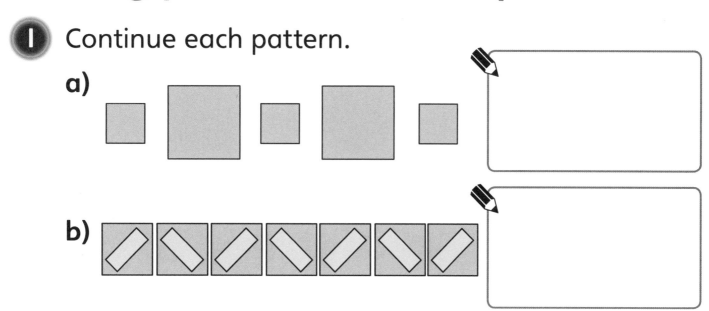

b)

2 Circle the missing shapes.

a)

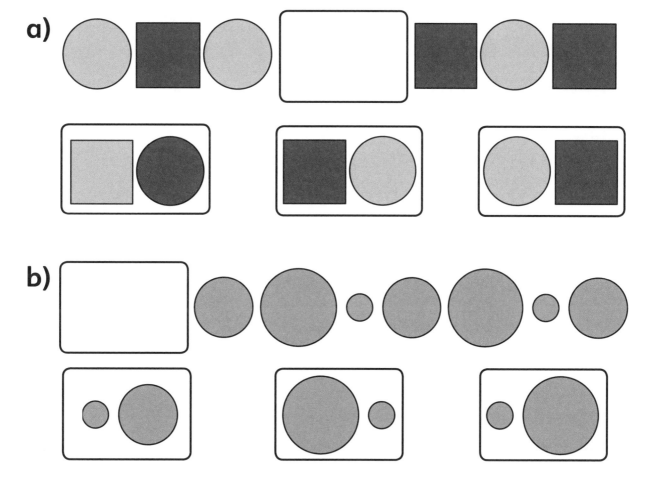

b)

3 Circle the repeating part. Complete the sentences.

The first one has been done for you.

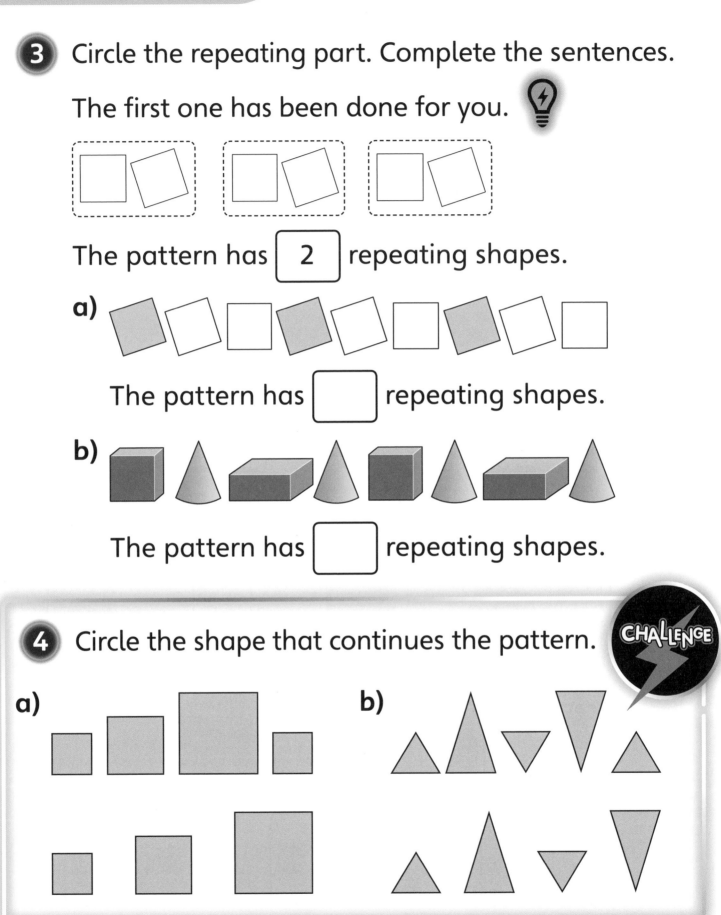

The pattern has | 2 | repeating shapes.

a)

The pattern has [ ] repeating shapes.

b)

The pattern has [ ] repeating shapes.

4 Circle the shape that continues the pattern. **CHALLENGE**

a)

b)

5 Complete the diagrams to continue the patterns.

a)

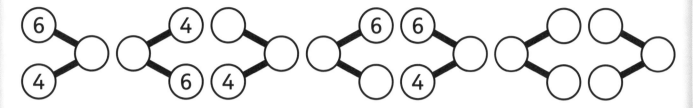

b)

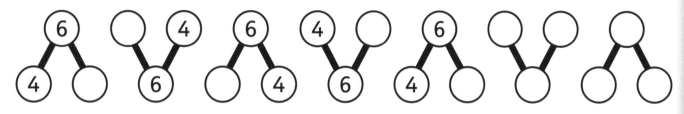

Reflect

Use any of these shapes to make a repeating pattern.

Cover up some of the shapes. Challenge your friend.

→ Textbook 1A p184

End of unit check

My journal

Where would you put this shape?
Explain why.

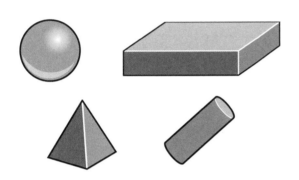

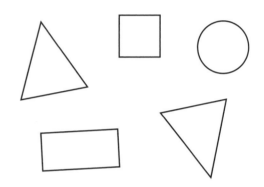

- I put the shape there because it _____

  _____

  _____.

These words
might help you.

dark **light**

shape

2D

3D **group**

134

Power check

How do you feel about your work in this unit?

Power puzzle

Choose three colours.

Colour the shapes so that shapes that are the same colour are only touching at a corner.

Find four different ways.

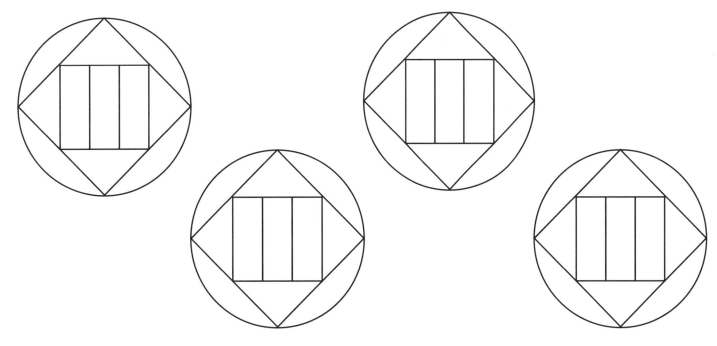

→ **Textbook 1A p188**

Counting and writing numbers to 20

1 How many  are there?

There are ☐ .

2 Show 12 on the ten frames.

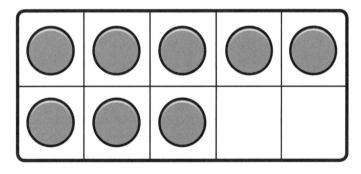
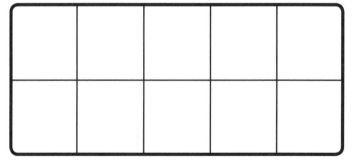

3 Complete the number line.

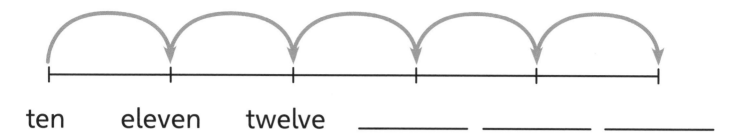

ten   eleven   twelve   _____ _____ _____

4 Complete the number line.

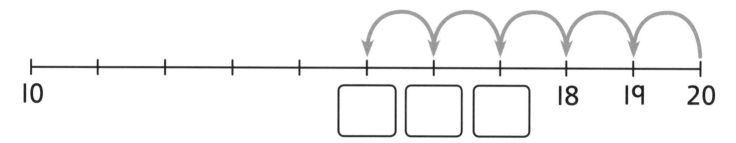

5 Fill in the missing numbers.

a)

10	11		13	14

b)

17		15	14

c) ☐ , 15, 16, ☐ , 18

d) 8, ☐ , ☐ , 11, 12

6 Explain Anna's mistake.

CHALLENGE

Eighteen, seventeen, sixteen, fiveteen, fourteen ...

I will try saying the numbers out loud.

Reflect

Think about what you have learned today.

- Today I have learned _____
- _____
- _____
- _____

Tens and ones

1 How many  are there?

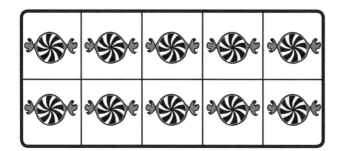

There is [ ] ten and [ ] ones.

There are [ ]  .

2 Show 16  .

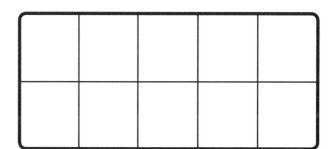

There is [ ] ten and [ ] ones.

3 Match the number sentences to the ten frames.

I ten and 2 ones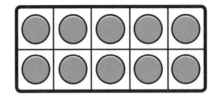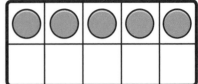

I ten and 7 ones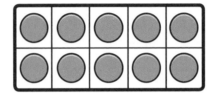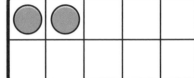

I ten and 5 ones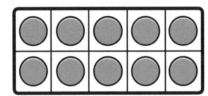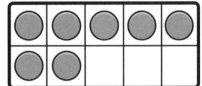

4 Fill in the boxes.

a) ⬜ = I ten and 6 ones

b) 19 = ⬜ ten and ⬜ ones

c) 10 = ⬜ ten and ⬜ ones

d) ⬜ = 2 tens

e) 0 tens and 7 ones = ⬜

5

I have 13 ones.

They are on a .

Complete the number sentence.

13 = ☐ ten and ☐ ones

6 How many ◯ are there?

CHALLENGE

Can I move some ◯ to help?

There are ☐ ◯ .

Reflect

Write down a number between 1 and 20.

My number = ☐ tens and ☐ ones.

Can you tell what number your partner made?

→ Textbook 1A p196

Tens and ones ②

1 How many ◯ are there?

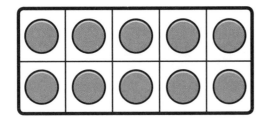 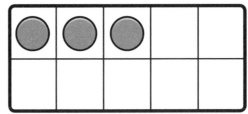

I ten and 3 ones = ☐

☐ + ☐ = ☐

There are ☐ ◯ .

2 Fill in the missing 🙂 .

How many 🙂 do you have?

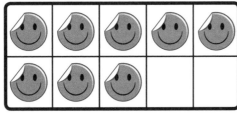 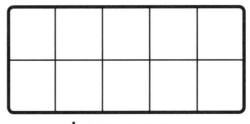

one ten   two ones

I ten and 2 ones = ☐

☐ + ☐ = ☐

I have ☐ 🙂 .

142

3

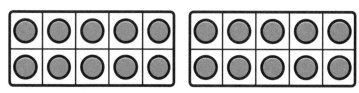

a) Circle 1 ten and 7 ones.

b) Circle 19.

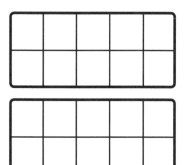

c) Show me 11.

4 Match the number sentences.

10 + 8   1 ten and 2 ones

10 + 10   1 ten and 8 ones

10 + 2   2 tens

10 + 0   1 ten

5 Prove Dan is right.

I can make 10 + 8 using ◯.

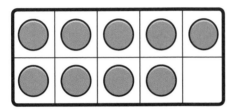 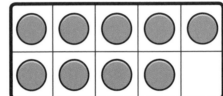

6 True or False?

16 = 1 + 6

_____

CHALLENGE

I think it is true!
16 is 1 ten and 6 ones
so 16 is 1 + 6.
Am I right?

Reflect

Write 15 in two different ways.

Counting one more, one less

1 There are 12 🚗 .

One more 🚗 arrives.

How many 🚗 are there now?

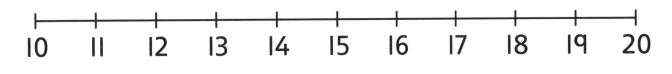

There are ☐ 🚗 now.

2 a) Show me one less than 19.

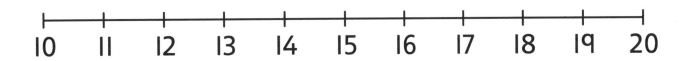

b) Show me one more than 10 + 5.

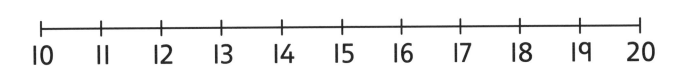

3 Complete the sentences.

a) One more than 13 is ☐ .

b) One less than eleven is _____ .

c) One more than 10 + 9 is ☐ .

d) One less than 1 ten and 5 ones is ☐ .

4 Complete the sentences.

a) ☐ is one more than 12.

b) _____ is one less than sixteen.

c) ☐ is one less than 2 tens.

d) Mark has 10 ◯ .

His mum gives him one more.

How many ◯ does Mark have now?

Mark has ☐ ◯ now.

5 Write more or less to complete each sentence.

a) 14 is one _____ than 15.

b) 18 is one _____ than 17.

c) 10 + 2 is one _____ than 11.

6 One more than ▢ is one less than ▢.

How many answers can you find?

Reflect

Write a number in the middle box.
Fill in the other boxes to show one less and one more.

one less	number	one more
▢	▢	▢

→ Textbook 1A p204

Comparing numbers of objects

1 Circle who has the fewest 🍪 and complete the number sentence.

Lena

Kai

12 ◯ 9

2 Circle who has the most 🧊 and fill in the number sentence.

Tess

Dan

☐ ◯ ☐

3 Write more or less to complete the sentences.

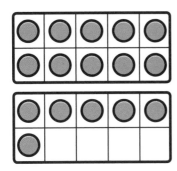 is _____ than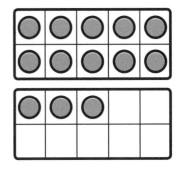

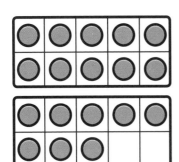 is _____ than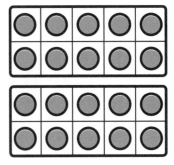

4 Complete the ten frames.

 is less than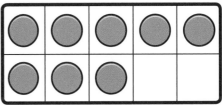

Is there more than one answer?

5 Emma has 15  .

Draw some  for Joe so he has more than Emma.

Emma	Joe

Reflect

How can I compare numbers of objects?

Comparing numbers

1 Write **greater than** or **less than** to complete the sentences. You can use the number line to help you.

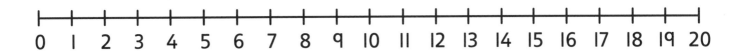

a) 15 is _____ 13.

b) 17 is _____ 19.

c) 10 + 5 is _____ 10 + 4.

d) 6 is _____ 16.

2 Use < or > to complete the number sentences.

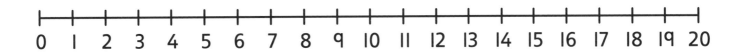

15 ◯ 13

17 ◯ 19

10 + 5 ◯ 10 + 4

3 Write the numbers. Use < or > to compare.

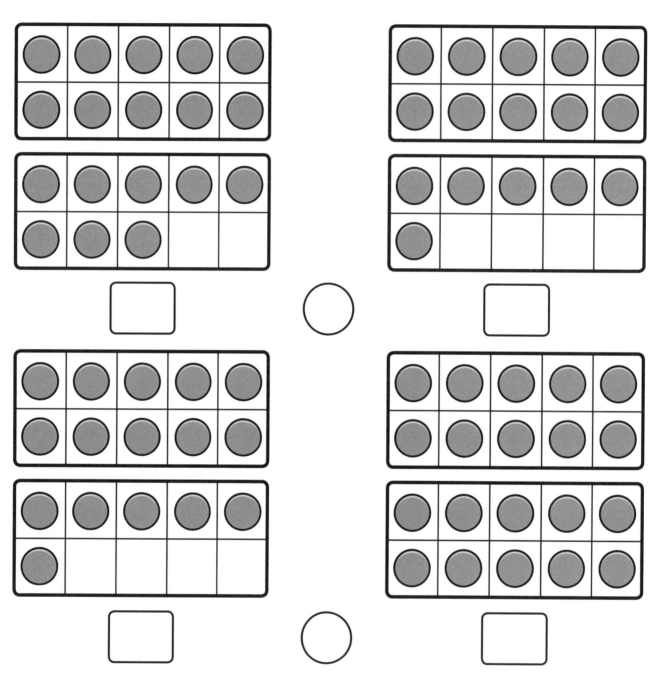

4 12 < ▢

How many answers can you find?

CHALLENGE

5 Fill in the boxes. Use each number once.

15   20   12

13   <   ☐

☐   >   9

15   =   ☐

6 Ben has 12 .

Mo has 1 more than Ben.

Use < or > to show this in a number sentence.

☐ ◯ ☐

Reflect

Use 4 different numbers to complete the number sentences.

☐ < ☐

☐ > ☐

→ Textbook 1A p212

Ordering objects and numbers

1 Draw 6 on the empty plate.

Anna
Billy
Dan

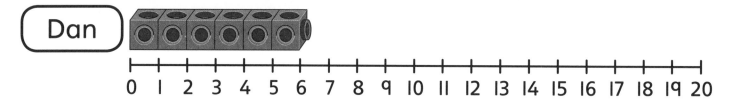

0 1 2 3 4 5 6 7 8 9 10 11 12 13 14 15 16 17 18 19 20

✔ who has the most .

✖ who has the least .

2 Order the numbers from largest to smallest.
Then complete the ⊞.

16   18   17

[ ]   [ ]   [ ]

largest   smallest

3 Order the numbers from largest to smallest.

9   15   12

[ ]   [ ]   [ ]

4 Compare 4, 14 and 9.

The smallest number is [ ].

The largest number is [ ].

Order the numbers from largest to smallest.

[ ] [ ] [ ]

5 Fill in the boxes. Use each number once.

12   20   17

13   <   ☐   <   ☐

☐   >   9   >   4

6 Sam has more  than Bilal.

Bilal has more 🍬 than Jan.

Jan has 14 🍬 .

How many 🍬 could Sam and Bilal have?

CHALLENGE

Can you prove it?

Reflect

14, 18, 16

Order these numbers in two ways.

- ○ _____
- ○ _____
- ○ _____

End of unit check

My journal

Which is the odd one out?
Explain why.

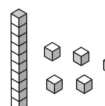

one more than 14

thirteen

10 + 5

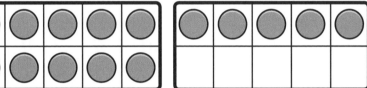

- The odd one out is _____

  because _____

  _____ .

These words
might help you.

tens   **ones**

more than   **less than**

Power check

How do you feel about your work in this unit?

Power puzzle

Complete the puzzle so every box has a different number.

| 9 | < | | < | 19 |

⬇ One more   ⬇ One less

| | < | | < | |

⬇ One more   ⬇ One less

| | < | | < | |

My Power Points

Colour in the ☆ to show what you have learned.

Colour in the ☺ if you feel happy about what you have learned.

Unit 1

I can …

☆ ☺ Sort and count objects to 10
☆ ☺ Count and write to 10
☆ ☺ Count back from 10 to 0
☆ ☺ Count one more and one less
☆ ☺ Compare and order numbers
☆ ☺ Use a number line

Unit 2

I can …

☆ ☺ Use a part-whole diagram
☆ ☺ Write number sentences
☆ ☺ Find different ways to make a number
☆ ☺ Make number bonds up to 10
☆ ☺ Compare number bonds up to 10

Unit 3

I can …

☆ ☺ Add parts to find a whole
☆ ☺ Find a missing part

☆ ☺ Find and make number bonds
☆ ☺ Find fact families
☆ ☺ Solve word problems

Unit 4

I can ...

☆ ☺ Find how many are left
☆ ☺ Break the whole into parts
☆ ☺ Find related number facts
☆ ☺ Find the difference between two numbers
☆ ☺ Solve word problems

Unit 5

I can ...

☆ ☺ Name 3D shapes
☆ ☺ Name 2D shapes
☆ ☺ Make patterns with shapes

Unit 6

I can ...

☆ ☺ Count and write numbers to 20
☆ ☺ Count using tens and ones
☆ ☺ Count one more and one less
☆ ☺ Compare numbers of objects
☆ ☺ Compare and order numbers

Wow! Look how
much we can do!